The Legends of the Nittany Valley

The Legends of the Nittany Valley

Henry W. Shoemaker

Nittany Valley Press

Published in the United States of America
by Nittany Valley Press
nittanyvalley.org

ISBN: 978-0-9853488-6-1
The Legends of the Nittany Valley
Shoemaker, Henry Wharton

"A Portrait of Henry Wharton Shoemaker" is excerpted from Popularizing Pennsylvania: Henry W. Shoemaker and the Progressive Uses of Folklore and History by Simon J. Bronner. It is reprinted by permission of The Pennsylvania State University Press Copyright © 1996 The Pennsylvania State University.

Henry Shoemaker photograph appearing on back cover used with permission of the Juniata College Museum of Art, Historic Photograph Collection.

Art and illustrations appearing in this book first appeared in Henry Shoemaker's original works, some of which are listed in the Abridged Bibliography.

Cover Photograph © William Ames
Back Cover Mural Photograph © Danielle Crowe
Back Cover Mount Nittany Photograph © Sam Panko
Design by Jonathan Hartland

Third Edition

"It is not likely that much, if indeed any part, of what I may write will be granted a permanent place in the literature of my country, nor am I stirred to effort by any ambition or dream that it may. I shall be well satisfied if, by what I write, some present entertainment be afforded to the reader, a love of nature inculcated, and encouragement given to a more manly or womanly life."

W.H.H. Murray

Contents

Editor's Note

This is an entirely new collection of cherished folklore of the Nittany Valley and nearby areas. With a few noted exceptions, the stories collected for this volume are excerpted from the many published works of Henry W. Shoemaker for their relevance to the Nittany Valley. Here you will discover the legend of Mount Nittany's fantastic origins, read about the magic of nearby Penn's Cave, and encounter other lore about the characters who appear in those tales. The legends themselves are reproduced exactly as they appeared in Henry Shoemaker's texts with original spelling, grammar, syntax, and idiosyncratic language wholly preserved and unaltered from their original versions. Each section includes its own original introduction, written especially for this collection to provide context and enhance the reader's appreciation and enjoyment. If you are interested in reading more of Henry Shoemaker's writing, the section at the very end of this book provides a list of sources from which these stories were assembled. The Abridged Bibliography of

Shoemaker will point you to an even wider selection of his writings. Certain of Shoemaker's books are available through Metalmark Books, an imprint of The Pennsylvania State University Press.

The image on the back cover shows a portion of the Mount Nittany Mural located at the State College Area School District's Fairmount Avenue Building, which today houses the Delta Program and once served as the local high school. The mural was created as part of a 1948 graduate thesis by Reba Esh, a Penn State graduate student. Dr. Viktor Lowenfeld, her adviser, organized the University's Art Education department. Esh's thesis involved organizing a collaborative "community mural" project modeled after the revitalization efforts of the time period that were sponsored by the Works Progress Administration. The students and townspeople involved in the mural's production chose to tell "the story of the Nittany Valley" by depicting the Legend of Princess Nittany. Its inclusion with this work provides not only an eye-catching visual, but also evidence of the ways in which myth and legend find expression in the life of our community. Thanks are owed to Danielle Crowe, Jon Downs, and Wilda Stanfield of the State College Area School District as well as Charolette Waltz of the Penn State School of Visual Arts for their assistance.

Thanks are also due to Dr. Simon J. Bronner for his scholarship and enthusiastic support. Dr. Bronner's portrait of Henry Shoemaker is both rich and lively. Thanks, as well, to Sheila Sager of The Pennsylvania State University Press for her warmth and helpfulness in making Dr. Bronner's scholarship available in this book.

A purpose of folklore is to pass along cultural memory across generations. Few have responded more vigorously or more effectively in conveying these stories than Dr. Ben Novak, from whom so many students and townspeople have come to know and love our legends and lore in the Nittany Valley's shadowy and candlelit places. A heartfelt and profound thanks to Dr. Novak.

A final and special note of thanks to Tom Shakely, without whom this book would not exist.

Introduction

    When we speak of the Nittany Valley, we should recognize that the Indians were here first. They gave their names to the places we inhabit today—Nittany, Waupalani and Bald Eagle, for example—and they first gave voice to the spirit of the place. Later came the pioneering educators and students of what would become The Pennsylvania State University, who breathed in and gave form to that spirit, even naming themselves for it: They became the Nittany Lions.

Little is known of the factual history of the American Indians in whose spirit we live today. Almost all that is known are their legends and stories, passed on by the few who survived in this area by the late nineteenth and early twentieth centuries. Fortunately, a young man from McElhattan, Henry W. Shoemaker (1880-1958), began hearing these stories as a boy. He made it his life's work to seek out all the Indian and settler story-tellers he could find, in order to record and publish them before their words disappeared into history.

Penn State students read these stories in the *Altoona Tribune*, where Shoemaker first published many of them, and then read the books in which he collected them. From him they learned the legendary origin of the Nittany Mountain, and the saga of the great Indian Princess who inspired it. The students chose her as their exemplar, and took her name as theirs. Several versions of this story, along with many others pertaining to the places and characters of this charming regional folklore, are collected here in *The Legends of the Nittany Valley*.

In the years since their initial publication, there has been much debate over the authenticity of the legends as products of a genuine oral tradition, with many historians suggesting that most if not all of them sprung from Shoemaker's fertile imagination. In considering the legends' impact on the people of the Nittany Valley, such questions, while undoubtedly relevant for scholars, are largely immaterial. Whether Shoemaker's stories are truly relics that have survived from our long forgotten past, products of his own creative impulse, or a bit of both (which is most likely), their influence is indisputable. For the purposes of this publication in particular, they should be taken at face value, not as historical artifacts that reveal the precise history of peoples past, but as unique stories—*our* stories—that evoke our common cultural history and confer greater meaning on our present.

Consider the unique power of myth to instill a sense of community.

George Lucas described one of his goals in making Star Wars as the creation of a new mythology for the modern age. From Darth Vader and Obi-Wan Kenobi to the Death Star and The Force, Lucas has furnished us with a remarkably flexible and re-silient contemporary common language with which to express timeless concepts like the quest for wisdom and the battle between good and evil. Today, people from around the country or the world can better communicate and relate through the shared language of myth. In this respect, it is no more relevant that the Star Wars mythology is only a few decades old, or that no one ever actually *believed* in Princess Leia, than it matters whether our own Princess Nittany walked among the American Indians hundreds of years in the past or was invented by yarn spinners from the turn of the century. References to Yoda, Han Solo or Luke Skywalker help us share sentiment in ways that are simple, direct and transferable across distance and culture. So too can our own local myths provide a sort of cultural shorthand for those who dwell, in body or spirit, in Central Pennsylvania.

The power of myth also grows from and strengthens a sense of place.

J.R.R. Tolkien spent years of his post-war life meticulously crafting the languages, legends and history of his imaginary realm before he took to writing *The Lord of the Rings*, or even its predecessor *The Hobbit*. So when Aragorn sings "The Lay of Leithian" an epic poem of the love and adventure of Beren and Luthien for Sam and Frodo while lapsing into Elvish or speaks with sadness of the fall of the Northern Kingdom, it lends an air of authenticity that draws the reader into the story. There can be no question that this attention to detail, employed throughout Tolkien's books to add flavor and depth to the storytelling, has contributed greatly to their enduring status as among the great works of Western literature. We are able to escape the daily humdrum to "inhabit" the world of Middle Earth because, despite the fantastical trappings, it feels like a real place, complete with its own folklore and history. With these, our own legends, which endow the Nittany Valley with its own mythic qualities, our special places can come alive in new and similarly magical ways.

Shoemaker once said, "No one can be truly happy who does not live in an atmosphere of the past, whether it be mental or actual." In telling these stories, we can discover both.

What is Mount Nittany? It is a geological formation whose distinctive slope is burned into collective memory, a place where generations of Penn State students have come to share camaraderie, conduct ritual, and even pursue romance, where we travel to find solace for peaceful contemplation, a symbol that means so much to the denizens of our Valley that more than once they banded together to preserve its unspoiled beauty for future generations. And perhaps... just perhaps... it is also a windbreak that rose up miraculously in one night to shield the fierce and lovely Princess Nittany from the wicked winds of the North.

To the extent that, for readers of these stories, it can become all of these at once, this book will have served its highest purpose.

While we can never travel to the Shire and visit Bag End or call forth a lightsaber using the power of The Force, we *can* catch an early morning glimpse of Mount Nittany as the rising Sun burns the mist from its peak or hike its trails and look down into our Valley from its many scenic overlooks. We can have our pictures taken at the Nittany Lion Shrine, participate in the annual Homecoming traditions, and find the spot of the Old Willow on the Willard Mall.

So while the Nittany Valley is, of course, a tangible, everyday place where people live and work, a magical kingdom lurks just beneath the surface, just waiting to be discovered by those with a pioneering and creative spirit. Revealing it is, at its very heart, the mission of The Nittany Valley Society, and it speaks directly to our purpose in publishing this book, which is to help the citizens of this community to take ownership of a shared mythology, one that helps solidify our grasp of a distinct, common identity in which we all can confidently take pleasure and pride.

The legends appearing in this work are only a small sampling of the total number of Indian and settler legends collected by Shoemaker. They are chosen for their relation and proximity to the Nittany Valley. Most locations are within less than an hour traveling time, and you can easily visit them. While some are mythical sites, there is enough information in the legends to actually locate where they are situated. But most are actual historical sites with markers. Visiting all of them will take you on journeys into places where story and history, imagination and myth, as well as timeless feelings merge. In doing so, you'll enter into the spirit of the Nittany Valley—the spirit that was here long before any of us arrived, and that will remain long after we pass through.

Enjoy these stories. Share them with friends and family, and carry them with you, especially upon returning to the idyllic Pennsylvania Valley cradled in the shadow of Mount Nittany.

Chris Buchignani
State College

I.

Princess Nittany and
Nittany Mountain

The legend of Princess Nittany has been the most fruitful of all the legends penned by Henry W. Shoemaker. Penn State's official website declares the story to be "invented by the author," and "purely fictitious," having "no basis whatever in fact." But even if true, it

doesn't matter. It has inspired the creation of two major organiza-tions—the Lion's Paw Alumni Association and the Mount Nittany Conservancy—to raise hundreds of thousands of dollars to preserve Mount Nittany as Penn State's proudest landmark. Thousands of students, alumni, townspeople, and visitors to the area climb Mount Nittany every year just to experience its magic. Indeed, our very identity as people of the "Nittany Valley" and as "Nittany Lions" springs from these legends that have helped to bind us in spirit.

Since first published by Henry W. Shoemaker in his book Juni-ata Memories *in 1916, the legend of Princess Nittany has been re-told in two additional versions. The first version below is Shoemak-er's original recounting of the legend, as he claims to have heard it from an aged Indian named Jake Faddy.*

The second version appeared shortly after. Although Penn State students may have heard the story independently of Shoemaker, the modern presumption is that when they came across Shoemaker's account, they liked it so much they decided to adopt elements of the story for their own special legend. In any event, the second legend below appeared in the 1916 student yearbook, LaVie. This rendition of the legend omits some of the salient facts of Shoemaker's story, such as the victory won by Princess Nittany's tribe over the southern tribes, and is told in much more flowery and elegant language re-flecting the literary tastes of the student body at that time.

The third version of the legend is of unknown authorship and date, but was adopted by the Mount Nittany Conservancy, Inc., to accompany the Conservancy's sale of engraved deeds to a square inch of Mount Nittany. The square inches are real—a piece of land 20'x20' was properly surveyed and divided into 57,600 square inch-es, and legally recorded in the Office of the Recorder of Deeds of Cen-tre County. This legend, however, differs in several respects from both the Shoemaker and student versions, especially in that it has Mount Nittany arising over the burial mound of Princess Nittany's

beloved, an Indian Brave named Lion's Paw, who was killed fight-
ing the "wicked wind of the North."

Nita-Nee:
A Tradition of a Juniata Maiden

One of the last Indians to wander through the Juniata Valley, either to revive old memories or merely to hunt and trap, his controlling motive is not certain, was old Jake Faddy. As he was supposed to belong to the Seneca tribe, and spent most of his time on the Coudersport Pike on the border line between Clinton and Potter Counties, it is to be surmised that he never lived permanently on the Juniata, but had hunted there or participated in the bloody wars in the days of his youth. He continued his visits until he reached a very advanced age. Of a younger generation than Shaney John, he was nevertheless well acquainted with that unique old redman, and always spent a couple of weeks with him at his cabin on Saddler's Run.

Old Jake, partly to earn his board and partly to show his superior knowledge, was a gifted story teller. He liked to obtain the chance to spend the night at farmhouses where there were aged people, and his smattering of history would be fully utilized to put the older folks in good humor.

For while the hard-working younger generations fancied that history was a waste of time, the old people loved it, and fought against the cruel way in which all local tradition and legend was being snuffed out. If it had not been for a few people carrying it over the past generation, all of it would now be lost in the whirlpool of a commercial, materialistic age. And to those few, unknown to fame, and of obscure life and residence, is due the credit of saving for us the wealth of folklore that the noble mountains, the dark forests, the wars and the Indians, instilled in the minds of the first settlers. And there is no old man or woman living in the wilderness who is without a story that is ready to be imparted, and worthy of preservation. But the question remains, how can these old people all be reached before they pass away? It would take an army of collectors, working simultaneously, as the Grim Reaper is hard at work removing these human landmarks with their unrecorded stories.

Out near the heading of Beaver Dam Run, at the foot of Jack's Mountain, stands a very solid-looking stone farmhouse, a relic of pioneer days. Its earliest inhabitants had run counter to the Indians of the neighborhood for the possession of the beavers whose dams and "cabins" were its most noticeable feature clear to the mouth of the stream, and later for the otters who defied the white annihilators a quarter of a century longer. Beaver trapping had made the stream a favorite rendezvous for the red men, and their campgrounds at the springs near the headwaters were pointed out until a comparatively recent date.

But one by one the aborigines dropped away, until Jake Faddy alone upheld the traditions of the race. There were no beavers to quarrel over in his day, consequently his visits were on a more friendly basis. The old North of Ireland family who occupied the stone farmhouse was closely linked with the history of the Juniata Valley, and they felt the thrill of the vivid past whenever the old Indian appeared at the kitchen door. As he was always ready to work and, what was better, a very useful man at gardening and flowers, he was always given his meals and lodging for as long as he cared to remain. But that was not very long, as his restless nature was ever goading him on, and he had "many other friends to see," putting it in his own language. He seemed proud to have it known that he was popular with a good class of white people, and his ruling passion may have been to cultivate these associations. On several occasions he brought some of his sons with him, but they did not seem anxious to live up to their father's standards. And after the old man had passed away none of this younger generation ever came to the Juniata Valley.

The past seemed like the present to Jake Faddy, he was so familiar with it. To him it was as if it happened yesterday, the vast formations and changes and epochs. And the Indian race, especially the eastern Indians, seemed to have played the most important part in those titanic days. It seemed so recent and so real to the old redman that his stories were always interesting. The children also were fond of hearing him talk; he had a way of never becoming tiresome. Every young person who heard him remembered what he said. There would have been no break in the "apostolic succession" of Pennsylvania legendary lore if all had been seated at Jake Faddy's knee.

Of all his stories, by odds his favorite one, dealt with the Indian maiden, Nita-nee, for whom the fruitful Nittany Valley and the towering Nittany Mountain are named. This Indian girl was born on the banks of the lovely Juniata, not far from the present town of Newton Hamilton, the daughter of a powerful chief. It was in the early days of the world, when the physical aspect of Nature could be changed over night by a fiat from the Gitchie-Manitto or Great Spirit. It was therefore in the age of great and wonderful things, before a rigid world produced beings whose lives followed grooves as tight and permanent as the gullies and ridges.

During the early life of Nita-nee a great war was waged for the possession of the Juniata Valley. The aggressors were Indians from the South, who longed for the scope and fertility of this earthly Paradise. Though Nita-nee's father and his brave cohorts defended their beloved land to the last extremity, they were driven northward into the Seven Mountains and beyond. Though they found themselves in beautiful valleys, filled with bubbling springs and teeming with game, they missed the Blue Juniata, and were never wholly content. The father of Nita-nee, who was named Chun-Eh-Hoe, felt so humiliated that he only went about after night in his new home. He took up his residence on a broad plain, not far from where State College now stands, and should be the Indian patron of that growing institution, instead of Chief Bald Eagle, who never lived near there and whose good deeds are far outweighed by his crimes.

Chun-Eh-Hoe was an Indian of exact conscience. He did his best in the cruel war, but the southern Indians must have had more sagacious leaders or a better *esprit de corps*. At any rate they conquered. Chun-Eh-Hoe was not an old man at the time of his defeat, but it is related that his raven black locks turned white over night. He was broken in spirit after his down-fall and only lived a few years in his new home. His widow, as well as his daughter, Nita-nee, and many other children, were left to mourn him. As Nita-nee was the oldest, she assumed a vicereineship over the tribe until her young brother, Wo-Wi-Na-Pe, should be old enough to rule the councils and go on the warpath.

The defeat on the Juniata, the exile to the northern valleys and the premature death of Chun-Eh-Hoe were to be avenged. Active days were ahead of the tribesmen. Meanwhile if the southern Indians crossed the mountains to still further covet their lands and liberties, who should lead them to battle but Nita-nee. But the Indian vicereine was of a peace-loving disposition. She hoped that the time would never come when she would have to preside over scenes of carnage and slaughter. She wanted to see her late father's tribe become the most cultured and prosperous in the Indian world, and in that way be revenged on their warlike foes: "Peace hath its victories."

But she was not to be destined to lead a peaceful nation through years of upward growth. In the Juniata Valley the southern Indians had become overpopulated; they sought broader territories, like the Germans of to-day. They had driven the present occupants of the northern valleys out of the Juniata country, they wanted to again drive them further north.

Nita-nee did not want war, but the time came when she could not prevent it. The southern Indians sought to provoke a conflict by making settlements in the Bare Meadows, and in some fertile patches on Tussey Knob and Bald Top, all of which were countenanced in silence. But when they murdered some peaceable farmers and took possession of plantations at the foot of the mountains in the valley of the Karoondinha, then the mildness of Nita-nee's cohorts came to an end. Meanwhile her mother and brother had died, Nita-nee had been elected queen.

Every man and boy volunteered to fight; a huge army was recruited over night. They swept down to the settlements of the southern Indians, butchering every one of them. They pressed onward to the Bare Meadows, and to the slopes of Bald Top and Tussey Knob. There they gave up the population to fire and sword. Crossing the Seven Mountains, they formed a powerful cordon all along the southerly slope of the Long Mountain. Building block houses and stone fortifications—some of the stonework can be seen to this day—they could not be easily dislodged.

The southern Indians, noticing the flames of the burning plantations, and hearing from the one or two survivors of the completeness of the rout, were slow to start an offensive movement. But as Nita-nee's forces showed no signs of advancing beyond the foot of Long Mountain, they mistook this hesitancy for cowardice, and sent an attacking army. It was completely defeated in the gorge of Laurel Run, above Milroy, and the right of the northern Indians to the Karoondinha and the adjacent valleys was signed, sealed and delivered in blood. The southern Indians were in turn driven out by other tribes; in fact, every half century or so a different race ruled over the Juniata Valley. But in all those years none of the Juniata rulers sought to question the rights of the northern Indians until 1635, when the Lenni-Lenape invaded the country of the Susquehannocks and were decisively beaten on the plains near Rock Springs, in Spruce Creek Valley, at the Battle of the Indian Steps.

As Nita-nee wanted no territorial accessions, she left the garrisons at her southerly forts intact, and retired her main army to its home valleys, where it was disbanded as quickly as it came together. All were glad to be back to peaceful avocations, none of them craved glory in war. And there were no honors given out, no great generals created. All served as private soldiers under the direct supervision of their queen. It was the theory of this Joan of Arc that by eliminating titles and important posts there would be no military class created, no ulterior motive assisted except patriotism. The soldiers serving anonymously, and for their country's need alone, would be ready to end their military duties as soon as their patriotic task was done.

Nita-nee regarded soldiering as a stern necessity, not as an excuse for pleasure or pillage, or personal advancement. Under her there was no nobility, all were on a common level of dignified citizenship. Every Indian in her realm had a task, not one that he was born to follow, but the one which appealed to him mostly, and therefore the task at which he was most successful. Women also had their work, apart from domestic life in this ideal democracy of ancient days. Suffrage was universal to both sexes over twenty years of age, but as there were no official positions, no public trusts, a political class could not come into existence, and the queen, as long as she was cunning and able, had the unanimous support of her people. She was given a great ovation as she modestly walked along the fighting line after the winning battle of Laurel Run. It made her feel not that she was great, but that the democracy of her father and her ancestors was a living force. In those days of pure democracy the rulers walked: the litters and palanquins were a later development.

After the conflict the gentle Nita-nee, at the head of the soon to be disbanded army, marched across the Seven Brothers, and westerly toward her permanent encampment, where State College now stands. As her only trophy she carried a bundle of spears, which her brave henchmen had wrenched from the hands of the southern Indians as they charged the forts along Long Mountain. These were not to deck her own lodge house, nor for vain display, but were to be placed on the grave of her father, the lamented Chun-Eh-Hoe, who had been avenged. In her heart she had hoped for victory, almost as much for his sake as for the comfort of her people. She knew how he had grieved himself to death when he was outgeneraled in the previous war.

In those dimly remote days there was no range of mountains where the Nittany chain now raise their noble summits to the sky. All was a plain, a prairie, north clear to the Bald Eagles, which only recently had come into existence. The tradition was that far older than all the other hills were the Seven Mountains. And geological speculation seems to bear this out. At all seasons of the year cruel and chilling winds blew out of the north, hindering the work of agriculture on the broad plains ruled over by Nita-nee. Only the strong and the brave could cope with these killing blasts, so intense and so different from the calming zephyrs of the Juniata. The seasons for this cause were several weeks shorter than across the Seven Mountains; that is, there was a later spring and an earlier fall. But though the work was harder, the soil being equally rich and broader area, the crops averaged fully as large as those further south. So, taken altogether, the people of Nita-nee could not be said to be an unhappy lot.

As the victorious queen was marching along at the head of her troops, she was frequently almost mobbed by women and children, who rushed out from the settlements and made her all manner of gifts. As it was in the early spring, there were no floral garlands, but instead wreaths and festoons of laurel, of ground pine and ground spruce. There were gifts of precious stones and metals, of rare furs, of beautiful specimens of Indian pottery, basketry and the like. These were graciously acknowledged by Nita-nee, who turned them over to her bodyguards to be carried to her permanent abode on the "Barrens." But it was not a "barrens" in those days, but a rich agricultural region, carefully irrigated from the north, and yielding the most bountiful crops of Indian corn. It was only when abandoned by the frugal redmen and grown up with forests which burned over repeatedly through the carelessness of the white settlers that it acquired that disagreeable name. In those days it was known as the "Hills of Plenty."

As Nita-nee neared the scenes of her happy days she was stopped in the middle of the path by an aged Indian couple. Leaning on staffs in order to present a dignified appearance, it was easily seen that age had bent them nearly double. Their weazened, weatherbeaten old faces were pitiful to behold. Toothless, and barely able to speak above a whisper, they addressed the gracious queen.

"We are very old," they began, "the winters of more than a century have passed over our heads. Our sons and our grandsons were killed fighting bravely under your immortal sire, Chun-Eh-Hoe. We have had to struggle on by ourselves as best we could ever since. We are about to set out a crop of corn, which we need badly. For the past three years the north wind has destroyed our crop every time it appeared; the seeds which we plan to put in the earth this year are the last we've got. Really we should have kept them for food, but we hoped that the future would treat us more generously. We would like a wind-break built along the northern side of our corn patch; we are too feeble to go to the forests and cut and carry the poles. Will not our most kindly queen have some one assist us?"

Nita-nee smiled on the aged couple, then she looked at her army of able-bodied warriors. Turning to them she said, "Soldiers, will a hundred of you go to the nearest royal forest, which is in the center of this plain, and cut enough cedar poles with brush on them to build a wind-break for these good people?"

Instantly a roar arose, a perfect babel of voices; it was every soldier trying to volunteer for this philanthropic task.

When quiet was restored, a warrior stepped out from the lines saying, "Queen, we are very happy to do this, we who have lived in this valley know full well how all suffer from the uncheckable north winds."

The queen escorted the old couple back to their humble cottage, and sat with them until her stalwart braves returned with the green-tipped poles. It looked like another Birnam Wood in process of locomotion. The work was so quickly and so carefully done that it seemed almost like a miracle to the wretched old Indians. They fell on their knees, kissing the hem of their queen's garment and thanking her for her beneficence. She could hardly leave them, so profuse were they in their gratitude. In all but a few hours were consumed in granting what to her was a simple favor, and she was safe and sound within her royal lodge house by dark. Before she left she had promised to return when the corn crop was ripe and partake of a corn roast with the venerable couple. The old people hardly dared hope she would come, but those about her knew that her word was as good as her bond. That night bonfires were lighted to celebrate her return, and there was much Indian music and revelry.

Nita-nee was compelled to address the frenzied mob, and in her speech she told them that while they had won a great victory, she hoped it would be the last while she lived; she hated war, but would give her life rather than have her people invaded. All she asked in this world was peace with honor. That expressed the sentiment of her people exactly, and they literally went mad with loyalty and enthusiasm for the balance of the night. Naturally with such an uproar there was no sleep for Nita-nee.

As she lay awake on her couch she thought that far sweeter than victory or earthly fame was the helping of others, the smoothing of rough pathways for the weak or oppressed. She resolved more than ever to dedicate her life to the benefiting of her subjects. No love affair had come into her life, she would use her great love-nature to put brightness into unhappy souls about her. And she got up the next morning much more refreshed than she could have after a night of sleep surcharged with dreams of victory and glory.

As the summer progressed, and the corn crop in the valleys became ripe, the queen sent an orderly to notify the aged couple that she would come to their home alone the next evening for the promised corn roast. It was a wonderful, calm, cloudless night, with the full moon shedding its effulgent smile over the plain. Unaccompanied, except by her orderly, Nita-nee walked to the modest cabin of the aged couple, a distance of about five miles, for the cottage stood not far from the present village of Linden Hall. Evidently the windbreak had been a success, for, bathed in moonlight, the tasseled heads of the cornstalks appeared above the tops of the cedar hedge. Smoke was issuing from the open hearth back of the hut, which showed that the roast was being prepared. The aged couple were delighted to see her, and the evening passed by, bringing innocent and supreme happiness to all. And thus in broad unselfishness and generosity of thought and deed the great queen's life was spent, making her pathway through her realm radiant with sunshine.

And when she came to die, after a full century of life, she requested that her body be laid to rest in the royal forest, in the center of the valley whose people she loved and served so well. Her funeral cortege, which included every person in the plains and valleys, a vast assemblage, shook with a common grief. It would be hard to find a successor like her, a pure soul so deeply animated with true godliness.

And it came to pass that on the night when she was buried beneath a modest mound covered with cedar boughs, and the vast funeral party had dispersed, a terrific storm arose, greater than even the oldest person could remember. The blackness of the night was intense, the roar and rumbling heard made every being fear that the end of the world had come. It was a night of intense terror, of horror. But at dawn, the tempest abated, only a gentle breeze remained, a golden sunlight overspread the scene, and great was the wonder thereof!

In the center of the vast plain where Nita-nee had been laid away stood a mound-like mountain, a towering, sylvan giant covered with dense groves of cedar and pine. And as it stood there, eternal, it tempered and broke the breezes from the north, promising a new prosperity, a greater tranquility, to the peaceful dwellers in the vale that has since been called John Penn's Valley, after the grandson of William Penn.

A miracle, a sign of approval from the Great Spirit, had happened during the night to forever keep alive the memory of Nita-nee, who had tempered the winds from the corn-patch of the aged, helpless couple years before. And the dwellers in the valleys adjacent to Mount Nittany awoke to a greater pride in themselves, a high ideal must be observed, since they were the special objects of celestial notice.

And the name of Nita-nee was the favorite cognomen for Indian maidens, and has been borne by many of saintly and useful life ever since, and none of these namesakes were more deserving than the Nita-nee who lived centuries later near the mouth of Penn's Cave.

Nittany:
The Legend of the Valley

Long, bright, ribbon of gold, blending, graying, into the deep blue of a twilight sky, set atop of a mountain line, rugged irregular; the breath of a night wind, soft, uncertain, rustling faintly across the broad expanse of tree tops; a thread of shining white in the valley just below her, all this Nittany saw and was thankful. Many were the moons and long, since her warrior went out to battle. Many were the flocks of wild geese that had flown northward and southward above her, and still, he had not returned. Manitou, Manitou the Mighty, was cruel, and yet-the south wind grew bolder and kissed her brown cheek, withered now and old; the dying light in the west lingered on her face, kindled answering lights in her eyes—another day was gone.

Down in the valley, lived an old warrior and his squaw. Weak, feeble, scarcely able to grind the corn or gather the berries which were their food, they lived alone, the remnant of a people once great and powerful. Frequently it had happened that just when the maize they had planted with so much labor was ready to reap, the north wind had come, bending the oak trees in his strong fingers, and had wrested it from them so that in the long winter there was little to eat.

And this Indian maid, since she was good and kind, had come down from her hilltop into the valley when all was dark, and had built a shield for them against the northwind, a barrier that even his strong fingers could not break. The old people saw this with wonder the thing that she had done, and called her Nittany, which means "wind breaker."

Then a great sickness came upon her and she died, and the old warrior and his squaw mourned her, and all who had known her mourned her; called her pious, called her good. And they built a mound over the place where she lay that her resting place might be remembered. Then in the night came the Great Spirit with thunderings and lightnings; the earth shook, great trees came crashing down and the people were sore afraid. After a time, the thunders grew duller and duller, the lightnings flashed less and less often, and peace, dark, silent, brooded over the valley. When the dawn came, the first pale light of morning, the people came forth and marveled; for in the place where they had builded the mound, now rose a great mountain. And they called it Nittany in honor of her who was called pious and good.

The snows of many winters had lain on the valley, many summers have come and gone. A new people had come up from the southward and taken possession of the land. Men with white faces had come from the eastward. There arose among this new people a great warrior chief named Woap-a-lanne, whom the men with white faces called Bald Eagle. He lived in this same broad valley, and he extended his hunting grounds far to the northward. Brave was he and led his warriors to victory, and many were the songs that the singers made in his honor of his bravery and his daring. Woap-a-lanne loved his brothers with the pale faces and made treaties with them and bartered with them under a great pine tree which still is standing. And when the time came that he should go to the Happy Hunting Grounds, even the white men mourned him and in his honor named mountains and valleys and even the creek that flowed thru his native valley with his name.

And again many snows and rains came. The people of Woap-a-lanne, they of the tribe of Lenni-Lenape grew fewer and fewer; the white brothers came and took their hunting grounds; and their mountains and valleys saw them no more.

Then in this broad valley, there rose the Great Mother, not of men but of minds of men. To her came the young men from many miles, and she taught them the wisdom of times past, taught them the use of tools, taught them the art of working. With her teaching was the sweetness, the gentleness, the goodness of Nittany, and into their hearts she instilled the bravery, the courage of Woap-a-lanne. And her sons went out into the world and worked with the arts she had taught them and brought back to her, honor and glory.

The world knew them; for in their minds was the gentleness of Nittany, in their hearts, was the strength of Woap-a-lanne.

The Legend of Mount Nittany

The famed Nittany Lion still strides the ledges and vales of the legendary Mount Nittany. It is as though he embodied the restless spirit of the mysterious Indian Princess Nit-A-Nee who gave her name to the Mountain, the Valley, and the Lion.

According to legend an old Indian warrior and his squaw once lived in the broad valley between the Tussey and Bald Eagle Mountains. Each year the crops they planted were wrested from their fields by a wicked North Wind in the autumn before the harvest. The valley was being deserted in the face of this Wind until a mysterious Indian maiden appeared who taught the tribe to build shields to hold against the wicked winds of the North.

The appreciative Indian tribe called the maiden Nit-A-Nee, which means "wind-breaker," and made her their Princess.

This Indian Princess fell in love with a handsome Indian brave of the tribe called Lion's Paw. This fearless Brave was killed in a fierce battle with the wicked wind from the North after his shield was stolen from him while he slept.

When she heard of Lion's Paw's death, Princess Nit-A-Nee searched every hill and dale of the land until she found the fearless Indian Brave's body, still standing even after he had died. She enfolded him in her arms and carried his still erect body back to a place in the center of the Valley where she laid the strong Brave in his grave and built a mound of honor over his strength.

On the last night of the full moon, after she had finally raised the last of the soil and stone over his high mound, a terrible storm came up unleashing itself with thunder and lightening and the wailing of a horrendous wind from the depths of the earth. Every Indian in the Valley shuddered and all eyes were directed to the Indian Brave's high mound upon which the beautiful maiden Princess Nit-A-Nee was mounted with arms outstretched to touch the sources of the lightning bolts in the sky.

Through the night they watched with awe as the Indian Brave's burial mound grew and rose into a Mountain penetrating the center of the big valley between the two legs of the Tussey and Bald Eagle ridges. When the dawn finally came a huge Mountain was found standing erect in the center of the Valley.

A legend had been born. The mound and the maiden had given place to a Mountain, and standing on its summit was a Lion surrounded by eleven orphaned male cubs, each of whom had the courage of the fearless Indian Brave and the heart of the mysterious Indian Princess.

From that day forward every place in the valley was safe, and the wind wrested nothing from the fields on which these Lions strode as fearless heroes from the Mountain. The people of the Valley from that date forward knew only happiness and bounteous plenty.

In the fullness of time men came from across the farthest seas to build a college at the foot of this Mountain. The strength and courage of the students of this college became known far and wide. In memory of the fearless Indian Brave and the mysterious Indian Princess, the students of the college erected posts on a field and fought their way across this field as the North Wind had once ravaged the fields of the ancient Indian warrior and his squaw.

As each student learned the destructive power of the North Wind across the fields, he also learned the strength of the Princess known as Wind Breaker, called in her language Nit-A-Nee, and the courage unto death of the Indian Brave called Lion's Paw. As long as this strength and courage is known in the Valley, Mount Nittany will stand as a breaker against the wicked Wind of the North.

It is passed on from generation to generation that, as long as the fields of the Valley resound each year to the reenactments of the battles between the wicked North Wind and the Indian Brave, the people who live in the valley will be happy and prosperous and safe.

But if the reenactments ever stop, Mount Nittany will lose its strength and disappear, and the wicked Wind of the North will stream down through the valley between the legs of the Tussey and Bald Eagle ridges, searing the land, wresting away all that has been planted and grown there, and scattering the tribes who live there. All the warriors and squaws of the place will then have to abandon the Valley and seek their homes in other places and climes, and learn the customs and ways of strangers.

This is the legend of Mount Nittany. May it stand forever high and strong in our midst, our breaker against the harsh winds of destiny and fate which sweep down from the North, the source of fearless courage and deathless love, both father and mother of the games by which we live.

May Mount Nittany ever rise above us as the Guardian before the gates of Old Penn State. May the mysterious Indian Princess ever stand in our midst as breaker and shield against the destructive power of the winds of fate. And may the Nittany

Lion's cubs forever join in the games which are the guarantee of the life of the land we love.

II.
Accounts of Battles
Affecting the Nittany Valley

The following two legends recount two battles affecting the Nittany Valley. The first legend, "The Old Tree: The Tale of a Vanished Landmark" recounts the details of the battle four or five hundred

years ago that drove Chun-Eh-Hoe, Princess Nittany's father, and his tribe, out of the Juniata Valley, resulting in the subsequent events recounted in the legends about Princess Nittany's reign and the rising of Mount Nittany described in Chapter I of this book.

The second legend, "The Story of the Indian Steps" recounts a battle more than three centuries ago, almost two centuries subsequent to Princess Nittany's reign, when the southern Indians once again sought to drive north over Tussey Mountain. This legend tells the story of the construction of the famous Indian steps up the southern slope of Tussey Mountain, which the southern Indians constructed to speed their invasion, and how Pipsisseway, the great chief of all the lands between Tussey and the West Branch of the Susquehanna to the north, cleverly defeated the southern Kishaquoquilas under Chief Silver Eagle.

With each of these legends, we gain a deeper sense of the importance of the Indian wars in central Pennsylvania prior to the arrival of the European settlers in this region, as well as a deeper perspective on the role of Princess Nittany in the history of the region.

The Old Tree:
The Tale of a Vanished Landmark

Close by the bank of the "Blue Juniata," facing the dark glen back of the picturesque borough of McVeytown, there stood for centuries, and until the flood of 1889 uprooted it and swept it away, a giant linden tree, a conspicuous landmark for generations of red men and white. During its latter years most of its top branches were gone, in fact little else remained except the main trunk with its tremendous girth, and hollow at that, to brave the storms. When the great flood swept down the valley, carrying everything before it, it seemed as if it sounded the tocsin of the new order of things. The grave, the quaint, the picturesque, the old-fashioned, all had to make way for the prosaic, matter-of-fact, dollar-mad world, which the coming twentieth century would usher in.

The stack, the forge, the foundry, the dynamo, the sand-rock quarry, the power house would render unsightly the pleasant nooks and peaceful valleys where the Indians once trod and which a hardier race of white men fought against aborigines and nature to possess. The great flood facilitated the vandalism which followed in its wake, the forces of discouraged nature swept out quickly what man with his axes, picks, gunpowder, and steam shovels had started to do laboriously.

And with the old log cabins, shady groves, giant trees, old fords, ferries, beaver dams, and reed-grown pools, went the legends, the folklore, the ghosts that lingered about these survivals of a simpler and happier day. And no one can be truly happy who does not live in an atmosphere of the past, whether it be mental or actual. The mechanical world may pile up bank accounts mountain high for the few, but it brings monotony, dreariness, empty pleasures, short life for the many. Oh, the joy of actually having seen the Juniata before the great flood, yet it only appears in the writer's eye of faith!

Toward the last days of the giant linden tree, in the year preceding the deluge, various propositions to cut it down were discussed. "It took up room in the field," "It gave no shade," "It was a rotten old shell," were a few of the wise reasons advanced for its elimination. But the spirit of procrastination that is the bane of many Pennsylvania farmers saved the tree until it might disappear with its generation! The fact that a very curious old legend of the early days of the Juniata Valley clustered about it had no weight with those having influence over the life of the tree. The old stories were "played out," so the shrewd young materialists held, better get rid of all the landmarks connected with them, there was not time for such trash.

If the truth must be told, the last fifteen years of the nineteenth century worked hardest on the old tales than any other period. It was an ugly period anyway, a period devoid of taste, as is evidenced by the hideous post offices, city halls, hotels and business blocks erected throughout Central Pennsylvania during those years. Their bareness and coldness typifies the material selfish aims of the builders, and the writer always hurries by them with a shudder and feels uncomfortable whenever he has to enter their inhospitable doors.

It appeared that for a number of years an aged Indian, called Old Israel, because of his Hebraic features, ranged through the Juniata Valley. He was probably the same savage who killed Joseph Campbell, the Indian trader, at the foot of the Tuscarora Valley, near Parnall's Knob, in 1744, but escaped punishment for political reasons. So with the lapse of years the bitterness felt toward him by the white race passed away, as he became welcome at many a farmhouse along the Juniata.

Like most of the wandering Indians, he was a noted story teller. It was an age when books were few, and farming folks had little time for reading, and to supply this want in their busy life, travelers, who put up for the night, were expected after supper to tell to the assembled household of their adventures on land and on sea, or of events in the stirring past. In this way the remnant of Indians became a class of professional story tellers, in a sense like the Celtic bards who cheered the long evenings in the Scottish farmsteads of the ancestors of the Juniata Valley's solid pioneers.

An Indian who had nothing to relate, who sat before the fire like a wooden image, would have to be a sterling workman or he would be apt to be turned away on his next visit.

As near as can be learned there were at one time nearly a hundred of these wandering Indian story tellers moving up and down the Juniata and other valleys. Their numbers gradually dwindled until they were all gone, and their places were taken, but not as well, by veterans of the Napoleonic wars, sons of old Indian fighters, drummer boys from the Revolution, great hunters, tinkers, traders, and peddlers.

Old Israel used to say that when he was a boy it was a part of an Indian's education to receive the oral history of his race from the old people. It was as necessary as the art of hunting, fishing, fighting. It was considered the highest attribute in education, of more importance even than the arts of war.

These old traditions were told in such an interesting manner that no young Indian ever forgot them. They knew the history of their people better than many of the white settlers, who after one generation forgot everything except that their people had been Ulster Scots or Germans, sometimes even getting their nationality mixed, but at best could not name the places in Ireland or the Palatinate where they originated, or the date when they arrived in Pennsylvania. It remained for those of their descendants who amassed fortunes in Pittsburg or Philadelphia to suddenly learn it all to the smallest branches, and grow from it an emblazoned "family tree."

Old Israel's favorite story related to the thrilling days when the Southern Indians, tiring of the confinement and struggling of their narrow valleys along the Maryland line, decided on the invasion of the peaceful and beautiful valley of the Juniata. The original Indians residing there were so happy and contented that they were utterly unprepared for war. As many of them were vegetarians, subsisting on dried fruits and nuts during the winter months, the manufacture of arrows and spears was becoming a lost art. Where there were no hunters there were no warriors. That was an old Indian maxim. But agriculture and fruit raising appealed more to these gentle Juniata Indians, they increased more in numbers and wealth by the arts of peace than by the arts of war. They never molested any of their neighbors to the north or south, did not expect to be molested in return. They were making rapid strides in art and music, their bards and story tellers possessed an oral literature as complete as many a white nation would be proud of to-day. Their king, Chun-Eh-Hoe, encouraged all that was best, and he and his family were greatly beloved.

After many generations of such peaceful development, it would have been folly to talk of "preparedness." Soldiers were a disliked class, no one wanted to think of a time when his ancestors fought, they were as undesirable ancestors as undertakers are to-day.

But during this blissful period a war-cloud was gathering among the Southern Mountains. It gathered in size and velocity until it swept into the happy vale of the Juniata.

One day when Chun-Eh-Hoe, surrounded by his devoted wife and family, were seated by the river bank in the beautiful garden spot now occupied by the Pennsylvania Railroad creosoting plant at Mount Union, that rare spot where Rev. Cyrus Jeffries dreamed of erecting a replica of the gardens of Versailles, listening to a famous bard recite a lengthy poem depicting the future greatness of his race, a band of citizens, dusty, wan and careworn, bowed low and asked to be heard in immediate audience.

As Chun-Eh-Hoe's court was democratic, the bard was motioned to desist for a few moments while the delegation of citizens expressed themselves. They hesitated to break the awful news to spoil the good king's peaceful rapture, but at length one Indian spoke as follows: "Sire," he began, "you are happy, you are good, you do not deserve to hear this, but it must be told. This morning a large company of Southern Indians, armed with spears and poisoned darts, came across the Blue Ridge through the gap a little to the southwest of Matawanna, and began murdering your peaceable subjects, sparing not even the women and children. No one was able to defend his home, the attacking force has already occupied several hundred acres on the southern bank of the Juniata. What shall we do to check their further advance?"

Chun-Eh-Hoe raised his hands in horror, his queen fell in a faint, the children wept with consternation.

"There is only one thing to do," he answered at length, "send messengers to every point in my domain informing my subjects of the invasion, and asking all men and boys to arm themselves with stakes and tomahawks, and advance from north, east and west on the cruel invaders."

The citizens then withdrew to the edge of the king's camp, where they conferred with their ruler's master of ceremonies. From him they secured a hundred fleet youths, who sped in every direction to spread the dreadful news.

Before sundown the male inhabitants of every encampment had armed themselves as best they could, some bore axes, tomahawks, celts, clubs, sharpened stakes, canoe paddles, every article of domestic use was brought into play as a weapon of war, and were on their way to the plains of Matawanna. When they came in sight of the fertile flat which lies between the Juniata and the foot of the Blue Ridge they could note that it was in hostile hands. Stockades were being run up, and smoke curled from the ruins of most of the cabins that had lately stood in this charming area.

Chun-Eh-Hoe, as gallant a figure no doubt as King Albert of Belgium, marshaled his volunteers for a night attack. The Juniata Indians knew every foot of ground, and thus figured an advantage over the strangers. Almost before the invaders knew that the Juniata forces had arrived they were attacked from the east and west, the Juniata line closing in on them and driving them back into the pass in the mountains. It was there that their superior weapons stood them in good stead, for they held a strong position until daybreak, when the attacking party withdrew.

The Juniata Valley was now free of its foes, but the dead which littered the plain were nearly all the subjects of Chun-Eh-Hoe. The king determined if possible to keep the Southern Indians in the gap, so he marshaled his forces in solid lines across the paths which led from the wild, deep glen.

As the morning advanced and no signs of attack were made, Chun-Eh-Hoe commenced breathing easily. He had just seated himself for dinner when a messenger ran up to tell him that a much larger attacking force of Southern Indians was crossing the Black Log Mountains, and threatening the royal encampment near Mount Union.

Chun-Eh-Hoe turned pale, and dropping his morsel of wild turkey breast, called some of his stoutest followers, and started with them in the direction of the royal campgrounds. When he got there he found that the enemy was in possession of all the lands on the south bank of the river, where they had massacred all the women and children. He was able to prevent the foes from crossing the Juniata, but could not dislodge them from the rich flats in Hill Valley and on Aughwick Creek.

In the morning he learned to his sorrow that his forces at Matawanna had been cut in two, and the Southern Indians were again in possession of the flats south of the river. At noon he heard of another huge attacking force that had crossed the Blue Ridge opposite the present city of Lewistown, and sweeping across the river was in full possession of the fertile plain as far north as the present site of Yeagertown.

Chun-Eh-Hoe's realm was menaced by three attacks, how could his poorly armed, untrained, pastoral subjects hold out against such hordes. But victory sometimes is hard won, and long deferred. The forces of Chun-Eh-Hoe, dominated by pure patriotism and love of their king, managed to hold possession of the Juniata Valley for more than a year.

But gradually the superior numbers of their foes were closing in on them, until all, including the women and children, were forced to make a last stand on the west bank of the Juniata, in and about that remarkable peninsula known as the "big elbow," near where Newton Hamilton now stands. There they were attacked by forces from the east, west and south and driven up Beaver Dam Run into Jack's mountain. Reduced in numbers, starving, and with the prospect of a long and severe winter there was no other course to pursue.

Chun-Eh-Hoe and his family were in the thick of the retreat, and sanguinary was the climb of Jack's Mountain with the attacking party always close at their heels.

On the summit a final stand was made, the Juniata Indians hurling rocks down on their pursuers, but they were again repulsed with great loss. The women carrying infants were compelled to run pell-mell down the steep slope in the direction of the present town of Belleville where another brave stand was made, but again the followers of Chun-Eh-Hoe had to break ranks and run in every direction in the cover of the autumnal forests to save their lives. It was a terrible defeat, a complete rout, and never again was the gallant king able to rally his people around him until they met in the broad valley at the headwaters of the Karoondinha, at what is now known as Penn's Cave.

Under the sheltering arched roof of the cave the fugitive monarch rested with his family and servants. Warm breaths, like from some cherishing mother, issued from the cavern's depths, bringing back life and almost hope. Scouts were sent out to find the stragglers who had survived the journey across the Seven Mountains, and they were congregated in the meadows about the cave, which far into the days of Indian antiquity had always been a region of good luck for the redmen.

But the spirit of the "original people" was unbroken. They had been driven from a beautiful valley, yet they had come into possession of a number of beautiful valleys, theirs was to be a broader destiny. And as the breaths of warm air issued from the giant cave they felt that they were still the favored of the Gitchie-Manitto.

Though outwardly calm and self-possessed, Chun-Eh-Hoe was sad at heart. Terrible melancholy, that awful sickness of the soul, rested heavily on him, he could see nothing except the memory of his defeat and rout. He busied himself apportioning homesteads and hunting grounds in the new territory. Thanks to the prevalence of game, there would be no starvation that winter. He looked after the spiritual welfare of the refugees, cheering the bereaved and sickly, though he had lost a kingdom and was bravest of all at heart. He worked with noble fortitude, sublime unselfishness, a true king. Never once did he utter a word of complaint, except when, to his family, he berated his own military ignorance, the unpreparedness of his nation.

"If we had been a race of hunters this never would have happened. Now I propose to encourage the royal sport of the chase, and the conservation of wild life."

Yet his soul was dying within him of humiliation, of chagrin, of sorrow for his dead followers. Over-conscientiousness was his greatest fault, and in this case a fatal one.

Vastly different was the attitude of O-Wan-Sa-Duta, king of the Southern Indians, at his camp at Matawanna. Though he had conceived the expedition into the Juniata Valley, he assumed no personal leadership of his forces. Clever generals arranged the details of the campaign, fought the battles and gave him the glory. He always kept himself at a safe distance in the rear of the belligerents, where, at an unfavorable sign, he could retire into his southern fortresses. He took no chances. If the invasion failed, and it couldn't as he had been preparing for it for ten years, he would still have his domain in the South with a smaller population to support. He was a wily, cruel savage, with love only for himself. Rumor had it that he had killed several successive wives, he neglected his children, and was civil only to flatterers.

Yet this was the king whom destiny was to lead into the Juniata Valley. Surely there must be some mistake in the lines of fate!

O-Wan-Sa-Duta was feeling in excellent spirits over the continued successes of his armies. There had been a demand from the victorious troops after every skirmish that he appear on the battlefront and receive the homage due his greatness, but he preferred the safe seclusion of his camp at Matawanna. He had given orders, however, that when Chun-Eh-Hoe and his followers had been finally driven beyond Jack's Mountain, and cut to pieces, that a swift runner should bring him the tidings. Then he might consent to review the victorious troops as they came back into the Juniata Valley through McVeytown Gap, but that question would be settled after he had received and digested the news.

After the rout, the generals selected the son of one of the commanders, a youth of sixteen, named Wa-Kan-Nah, noted for his fleetness of foot, to carry the glad tidings to the august monarch. The lad was overcome with joy at this signal honor, but managed to get started promptly on his ten-mile run across the steep mountains. Without a pause or a misstep he ran at breakneck speed, outdistancing the swiftest birds. Within his mind was the fixed idea to bring the glorious tidings to the monarch in less time than any one else could have done it. He would do in an hour or less what would take most runners one hundred minutes to accomplish. His brain aflame with pride and love for his king, he plunged on, his black hair streaming in the wind, clearing rocks and rivulets, bounding up the steep slopes of the mountains like a deer.

In an incredibly short space of time, a minute or two less than an hour, he was at the bank of the Juniata, on the opposite shore of which was his king's headquarters. Dripping with perspiration, his heart thumping against his breast, his eyes popping from his head, he sprang into the icy current. Swimming with desperate strokes he was soon on the east bank, and another bound or two brought him in front of O-Wan-Sa-Duta's cabin. There he was halted by a sentry, who struck him across the chest with a pike, knocking his breath away. When he recovered, he demanded the cause of such unseemly conduct. The sentry told him gruffly that the king was asleep; he wanted no disturbances outside of his apartment.

Wa-Kan-Nah, taken aback, informed him that he had brought news of a complete victory over Chun-Eh-Hoe, it must be conveyed to the king at once.

The sentry shook his head. "My orders are to let his majesty sleep. They cannot be disobeyed."

So the exhausted and disappointed messenger prepared to wait his king's pleasure, his slim body swept by the bitter east wind from the river. His head became dizzy, he felt chilly, and an unsteadiness came into his long thin legs. An old man, a soothsayer, from one of the southern valleys, who had been waiting two days for an audience with the king, noted the boy's symptoms of exhaustion and handed him his staff, a long linden pole, to lean upon.

Wa-Kan-Nah rested his tired form on it, and his weight bore it into the freezing ground. His head became dizzier, his frame rocked, and he swung around like a top, and in a few minutes he lay at the foot of his staff, stone dead.

At dark, when the king awakened from his twenty-four hour doze, his servants informed him of the great victory, of the cutting to pieces of the forces of Chun-Eh-Hoe, and how within an hour after the foe had fled, the news was at his royal camp.

Then one of the lackeys added, "And the dispatch runner, a youth named Wa-Kan-Nah, son of one of your commanders, dropped dead."

The king rolled over on his couch and muttered, "Dropped dead, eh? He must have been a weakling. Throw his cursed corpse into the river."

Then he turned his back on his servants and began snoring. The attendants withdrew and did as their master ordered, pitching the lifeless form of the brave messenger into the cold torrent, swept with the autumn winds. But they forgot to remove the long staff, the pole of linden, on which he had leaned so heavily, that it penetrated the cold earth. And it was destined to take root, and next spring, when O-Wan-Sa-Duta had moved his royal lodge house to the meadows at Mount Union, it blossomed forth into pale green foliage. Stronger and bolder it grew, until it became an arboreal giant of vast height and girth, watching the dynasties of kings rise and fall, the centuries pass as days, braving all storms, except the driving flood of 1889, which eventually carried it away.

The Story of the Indian Steps

It was at the foot-races between the Indians south of the Tussey Mountains and the Indians north of these mountains, which took place on the "plains" near what is now Pine Grove, that Silver Eagle, ruler of the Kishoquoquilas, or Southern Indians, saw his cousin, the beautiful Princess Meadow Sweet. He had not laid eyes on her since she was carried away when the Northern Indians, or Susquehanalis, overran the Southern country and killed her father, King Yellow Thistle. She had been a nominal captive since her sixth year, and she was now sixteen. Ironwood, the mighty warrior and King of the Susquehanahs, who invaded the Southern country, had adopted her, and her beauty and intelligence made him lavish on her more affection than on his own children. At his death his eldest son, Pipsisseway, or Prince's Pine, inherited the rulership of the vast domain which included all the territory now known as "northern," "central," and "western" Pennsylvania. He greatly admired his exquisite-looking foster-sister Meadow Sweet, who in turn looked up to him on account of his sterling character, intrepid military skill and giant strength. The young monarch had always called her his "little sister," and looking upon her as such, romantic impulses were not stirred within him as early as they might otherwise have been.

When old Iron wood was dying he begged his sons to see that Meadow Sweet received a dowry on her marriage. Pipsisseway promised the expiring ruler that she should have "all the lands which lay east of Spruce Creek, south and west of the Susquehanah and north of Jack's Mountains." There was a smile on the aged chieftain's lips when he heard this, and in another hour he was dead. None mourned him more than his foster-daughter, for there was a deep sympathetic bond between them. Pipsisseway carried out his promise, which made Meadow Sweet possessor of a domain of singular beauty and natural wealth. And this territory became speedily known under the poetic title of "The Land of Meadow Sweet."

Thus it was described in Indian oratory and in agreements with distant tribes. There may have been a "love motive" back of Pipsisseway's generous suggestion, as it would seem unusual to present a foster-sister with a territory comprising some of the richest land in what is now Central Pennsylvania. It even included the royal campgrounds, burial grounds and pottery works which were located in what is now Wayne Township, Clinton County. This beautiful retreat, known to the first white settlers as "Patterson's Town," had been the favorite headquarters for the great chieftains for centuries, and unless Pipsisseway intended marrying Meadow Sweet he would be forced to move the royal lodge-houses and abandon the graves of his ancestors if she became the wife of another. It may have been her extreme youth that prevented his open love-making, or some secret understanding between the girl and himself that the betrothal was not to be announced until some future date. The princess was treated with the greatest deference by Pipsisseway and his three brothers, Oheckerberry, Red Pine and Moonseed. Most of her time was spent at the royal encampment by the Susquehanah, where she was attended by a score of maidens, the daughters of noted war-chiefs. Wise men, from beyond the Allegheny Mountains and from the far South, instructed her in all the arts and sciences known to the redmen. She was taught the use of the bow and arrow, and dart. The mysteries of woodcraft were explained by the greatest hunters that could be summoned for that purpose. Her life was a happy one, surrounded by congenial company, and, living in a beautiful region, she had little to wish for.

During important religious ceremonials or sporting events she accompanied Pipsisseway to different parts of his domain. It had hitherto been deemed wise not to encourage any athletic competitions with other Indian kingdoms, but the Kishoquoquilas had challenged so repeatedly that the Council of Wise Men, after grave deliberation, advised Pipsisseway to allow it to be accepted. These Wise Men knew that in their realm resided the fleetest runners, jumpers, wrestlers, and weight throwers, and no challenging party would stand any chance against them. They considered it would be humbling to the pride of their opponents to give them a decisive defeat in the field of sport and make them feel less likely to stir up warfare. This was logic, but they omitted to figure in the effect of the presence of Princess Meadow Sweet, stolen in her early childhood from the Kishoquoquilas, upon the horde of warriors from the South. The great athletic meet took place the latter part of May, when nature was at her loveliest. The "plains" where it occurred were just north of the mountains which formed the boundary between the two rival kingdoms. They had been formed by fires frequently burning the timber, which had eventually fallen down, and the ground pastured smooth by vast herds of buffaloes, elks, moose, and deer. The sports were to continue during four days and at night love feasts were to be held for the visiting redmen to become better acquainted with their neighbors. The greatest precautions were made to have everything pass off pleasantly. Pipsisseway, who was a diplomat as well as a warrior, called all the athletes before him in a private audience, urging them in no case to defeat a Southern Indian by a wide margin.

Every finish was to be close, and if it looked as if the Susquehanahs were to roll up a huge score of points against their competitors, some events must be purposely lost. This was a slightly different program from the one advised by the Wise Men, who urged that the Northern athletes give a decisive beating to their rivals.

The weather was ideal for the tournament, and the number of Indians present far exceeded anticipations. They came from every direction, marshaled by their chiefs. It was twenty years since the last contest of this kind had taken place. The Susquehanahs had been victorious by a wide margin, and the Kishoquoquilas had returned across the mountains in an ugly frame of mind. On several occasions they had sent expeditions to the North, which, though always repudiated by King Yellow Thistle, inflicted serious damage on unprotected Northern tribes. The direct result of the athletic games had been King Ironwood's great invasion of the South, ending with the killing of Yellow Thistle and the capture of his young daughter. Ten years had passed, and the jealousy of the Kishoquoquilas, while not wholly appeased, was apparently not at a very acute stage. Embassies protesting friendship and laden with gifts had visited Pipsisseway after his father's death. The first challenge for an athletic tournament had been made in a friendly spirit. Had it been accepted at once, the unpleasant features which later clustered about it might have been averted.

Pipsisseway was young, and referred the matter to his Council. They voted against it unanimously, so the challenge was rejected. Later when Pipsisseway heard the disagreeable talk occasioned he regretted what had been done. When he discussed it with the Councillors they told him that the previous tournament had brought on a bloody and senseless war. This one would do the same. When a second challenge arrived it was rejected on similar grounds. Had the third challenge been refused, war would undoubtedly have resulted. Pipsisseway said if the meet were held and no ill-feeling resulted, it would show that he was as great a ruler as the greatest of his ancestors.

None of them had ever sanctioned an athletic contest with the Kishoquoquilas that had not ended in a war. This was as sure as the sun would rise in the morning. Pipsisseway surely wanted no wars during his reign. He wanted to make an agricultural people out of his subjects; wars and disease had made awful inroads in the Indian population. He would recoup their numbers. He was the first man on the American continent to preach against race suicide. Not that Indians willfully prevented large families, but the mothers were often ignorant or careless, consequently infant mortality was high. Prizes were offered for large families, and to mothers who were able to raise their children beyond the "dangerous age" where children's diseases were most fatal. Prizes were offered for the largest patches of cleared land, the largest yields of crops, the most substantially built lodges, for the scalps of dangerous animals and the like. Pipsisseway was essentially a "constructive monarch."

A description of his personal appearance has come down to us, and is strangely like that of the most constructive American of the present day, Col. Theodore Roosevelt. He was, of course, darker than the Colonel, but like him was of medium height, powerfully built, and with prominent, aggressive teeth. Unlike his modern prototype, he died at an early age, but he ranked as the greatest Indian King Central Pennsylvania ever possessed. He was simple in his habits, being extremely democratic and affable. His subjects, who numbered about fifty thousand souls of different tribal characteristics and residing vast distances apart, all worshiped him, and would have laid down their lives for him without a murmur.

When he appeared at the "plains," accompanied by his faithful brothers, and his foster-sister Meadow Sweet, he was greeted with the wildest enthusiasm. As a personal tribute nothing like it was known in Indian annals. Many old men said that the bulk of the vast turnout of people was due to a desire to see the popular monarch rather than to witness the contests. Fewer Indians would have tramped a hundred miles to see races alone. They had come from the headwaters of the Allegheny, the Chemung, the Lycoming, from Chillesquaque, Shamokin and Mahantango, ostensibly to see a magnificent tourney, but in reality to show their loyalty to their King. Unlike other Indian rulers; and some of lesser rank, Pipsisseway did not travel in a litter. He walked every foot of the way from the Susquehanna to the Spruce Creek Valley. His brothers also walked, but insisted that Meadow Sweet ride in a litter. She reluctantly consented, as she had absorbed her foster relatives' democratic spirit. Horses were unknown in those days, but sometimes the priests rode elks and moose in religious pageants. As these animals were only ridden on sacred occasions, races between Indians mounted upon them would have been impossible. The first event was a foot-race from the head of the plains to the Rock Spring and return. Two champion runners, one representing the Susquehanahs and the other the Kishoquoquilas, started on a signal given by Meadow Sweet, who waved a bunch of heron's feathers. The Susquehanah runner leaped to the front and led his Southern competitor by several hundred yards. There was silence in the Kishoquoquilas camp, and not too much applause among the Susquehanahs, as they had been warned not to display undue enthusiasm lest it anger their rivals. The race seemed like a procession until the last hundred yards, when the Susquehanah runner seemed to tire badly.

His Southern rival crept upon him amid the terrifying yells of his cohorts, but the Susquehanah managed to last long enough to win by a foot. The Southern Indians were delighted with the result, but they little knew that the Susquehanah runner had only feigned fatigue, and could have won by several hundred yards, if he wished. The second event was a twenty-mile point-to-point relay race, which the Susquehanahs could have won easily, but they held back and only allowed themselves to win by a narrow margin. The first day's sport ending without ill-feeling of any kind, Pipsisseway felt much encouraged. A magnificent banquet was spread under the white oaks, which was attended by King Silver Eagle, of the Kishoquoquilas, his retinue, as well as Pipsisseway, his brothers, retainers, and the Princess Meadow Sweet. Silver Eagle was presented to the princess, whom, as already stated, he had not seen in many years, since she was carried off by the conquering invader, Iron wood. Although she was his cousin, Silver Eagle fell in love with her instantly.

He was very attentive to her all through the evening, but she kept him at a distance, being discreet enough not to want to offend him, but at the same time not caring to arouse Pipsisseway's jealousy. She was woman enough to feel that underneath her foster-brother's calm exterior, there smoldered a deep interest for her. She admired him, and was only waiting for him to say the word, when she would gladly agree to become his wife. Silver Eagle laid great stress on their relationship, and suggested now that the feeling between his tribes and the Susquehanahs were so thoroughly amicable that, accompanied by a proper bodyguard, she be allowed to pay a visit to her old home south of the Tussey Mountains. She told him that she would love to do this some time, and felt confident her kingly foster-brother and guardian Pipsisseway would gladly give her permission. At midnight the visitors retired to their quarters, and every one in authority among the Susquehanahs breathed easier. The first day's festivities had come and gone, and everybody was happy. On the next day took place the jumping contests and shooting matches. At high-jumping and broad-jumping the Susquehanahs excelled, but they were careful not to win too easily from the Kishoquo-quilas. The shooting was the most interesting part of the entire tournament. There were contests at archery, participated in by trained warriors, by aged warriors, by small boys and by women. In all these classes, Susquehanah prowess prevailed, but only by the narrowest of margins. The Kishoquoquilas were beaten, but not disgraced. The Indians from the South were still hopeful they might win something before the contest ended, and exhibited no ill-feeling.

That night King Pipsisseway dined a select company under the white oaks. The only outsiders were Silver Eagle and his per-sonal suite. He renewed his attentions to Meadow Sweet, paint-ing to her in lurid colors the beauties of the Southern Country, its valleys, its mountains, its rivers, its population so intelligent and handsome compared to those in the North. "They are your peo-ple," he said, "you must mingle with them; you will love them as much as they love you. You know how they cheer you every time you appear at the tournament." Meadow Sweet continued her tactfully guarded conduct, and Silver Eagle departed at the midnight hour, in excellent humor. "You are a born diplomatist," said Pipsisseway to her after the distinguished guest had gone." You were born to rule over vast dominions. The world has never seen your equal in womankind."

Meadow Sweet smiled to herself; Silver Eagle's attentions were arousing the latent fire of Pipsisseway. Probably the crowning event of the tournament would be his public announcement of their betrothal. But he hadn't proposed as yet. She knew full well who she was, and how at a word from herself Silver Eagle would demand her restoration to the Kishoquoquilas. But she would remain where she was for two considerations. Being a woman, she had no inheritance beside her rank in her own country; with the Susquehanahs she had inherited a large territory, and had a chance of becoming the Queen of King Pipsisseway, if he proposed. With the third day took place the wrestling matches, the live-bird shoots, the weight-throwing competitions and the grand animal drive. The Susquehanah wrestlers and weight-throwers were the victors, but their rivals apparently put up good fights.

Ten thousand live wild pigeons and parrots were shot at in the live-bird competition, the majority of which were killed by the Susquehanahs. Then came the animal drive. A thousand buffaloes, elks, moose, and deer were released one by one from a corral and driven across the plains. The idea was to kill an animal at the first shot. If it did not fall it scored one against the party who held the bow. Out of the thousand animals seven hundred fell at the first bow thrust. Of these, three hundred and forty-nine were killed by the Susquehanah nimrods, so carefully had they measured their skill against their opponents. The Kishoquoquilas had won an event, so were happy. That evening Silver Eagle was again entertained at Pipsisseway's quarters. He was in excellent spirits and monopolized so much of Meadow Sweet's attentions that Pipsisseway almost felt slighted.

This was especially so when he began talking to her in his Southern dialect, as if to cut Pipsisseway entirely out of the conversation. Meadow Sweet was glad when he left, and threw herself at full length at Pipsisseway's feet, exclaiming, "Oh, how he tires me."

"I'll be glad when this is all over, just to get rid of Silver Eagle," said Pipsisseway.

The next day's program consisted of several minor contests, such as a three-legged race, a race for cripples, and a dart-throwing competition. These the Susquehanahs let the Kishoquoquilas win. The score of the tournament stood fifty-five to forty-five; the Susquehanahs had "played their cards well." After these contests, a magnificent barbecue took place, and the beasts slain in the animal drive the day before were served up, deliriously cooked, to the multitude. It was estimated that ten thousand Indians "partook" of the repast, but in what proportion seven hundred animals could go into ten thousand rapacious Indian stomachs is a question for an expert hotel-keeper, and not for an historian. A private repast was served under the white oaks by Pipsisseway, as a parting honor to King Silver Eagle, his retinue, and staff. Antelopes brought from what is now Kentucky were served to these dignitaries, as was green corn and tomatoes preserved in their natural state from the year before. Silver Eagle was crouched close to Meadow Sweet while the feast was in progress, and whispering compliments in her ears. After the meal was over he contrived to edge her into a quiet corner, where he could talk to her undisturbed. "I love you, fairest cousin," he expostulated, "I can keep back these words no longer. Come with me tonight; we shall be married with great pomp, and you shall rule with me over my dominions. You belong to our people by birth; you are an alien among the Susquehanahs." Meadow Sweet fully expected this outcome, and was prepared to meet it. It was a trying position, as to give an excuse that would not insult her admirer took considerable tact. "I am honored by your proposal, famous cousin," she replied, "but you are aware that I am a captive, though a willing one, of Pipsisseway; I am also very young; my power of choice is vested in him as my guardian. Ask his permission; I shall be guided by his noble sense of fairness." Silver Eagle could not tell whether it was "yes" or "no," but was not displeased. He took the maiden's hand in his and kissed it. "We will go at once to your worthy guardian, Pipsisseway, who is not the man to hinder a cause like true love." Pipsisseway had been pretending to be holding a conversation with some of his chiefs while this little talk was in progress, but he had been watching the two actors carefully.

He was especially anxious to note any sign in Meadow Sweet's face indicating that she possessed a lurking interest for her cousin. Being impressed by her lack of concern, he was determined to outwit the wily interloper. Of course, he could not be sure that Silver Eagle had been proposing, but it looked very much that way. When the Southern monarch and Meadow Sweet approached, and the retainers fell back leaving the trio together, he was prepared for any emergency. "Worthy King, I have come to ask your foster-sister's hand in holy marriage," said Silver Eagle. "Gracious ruler, I much regret to say that I have promised her in marriage to myself" replied Pipsisseway. This was a stinging blow to Silver Eagle's hope and pride; his black eyes snapped angrily; he staggered like a drunken man.

When he recovered himself he said, "Is this true, fairest cousin?" Meadow Sweet, while Pipsisseway had never proposed to her, would have taken him any time if he had, was only too glad to answer, "It is the truth." "Then, why didn't you tell me so a few minutes ago, and save me this humiliation?" said Silver Eagle with renewed anger. "I am, great king, as you are aware, only a captive of Pipsisseway's; I could not answer for myself. But I can truthfully say that I love him with all my heart." Pipsisseway smiled at this clever rejoinder, and held out his hand in a friendly manner to Silver Eagle. The Southern monarch put his own hand behind his back, and edged away from him, muttering to himself. Pipsisseway walked after him, but he refused to notice him. The four days' festivities had wound up in a quarrel after all. There was no use trying to pacify Silver Eagle; he had probably been mad all along over the almost continuous victories of the Susquehanahs in the tournament, but now had come "the unkindest cut of all."

Early in the morning it was reported that Silver Eagle had broken camp at dawn, and withdrawn across the Tussey Mountains. There were a number of unpleasant incidents between the Kishoquoquilas and the Susquehanahs over the breaking up of camp; several unprovoked murders were committed by the Southern Indians, and threats of all kinds passed. Their King's disappointment, though unknown to them, was evidently telegraphed to them in some form of unrest, and all the ugliness in their natures came to the surface on "moving day." Nothing further was said about the marriage of Pipsisseway and Meadow Sweet until they had returned to the royal camping-grounds on the Susquehanna, There the betrothal was publicly announced, and fleet runners sent to all quarters of the realm to acquaint the various tribes of the gladsome news. This, coming so soon after the signal victory over the Kishoquoquilas in the athletic tournament, stirred the Susquehanahs into a white heat of patriotism. It would have been a good time to go to war; every one was in a mood to fight for his country. The wedding took place "two moons" after the betrothal was announced, being attended by fully five thousand Indians, as many Susquehanahs who had witnessed the athletic tournament. Ambassadors were present from all the neighboring kingdoms, with the one notable exception of the Kishoquoquilas. This was accounted extraordinary, as Meadow Sweet, being a Kishoquoquilas princess, the daughter of their late King Yellow Thistle, should have married in the presence of some of her own countrymen.

A brief honeymoon was taken to Lewis' Lake, a spot sacred to the Indians as having been once the entrance to the Underworld, or realm of spirits. Upon their return, the Council of Wise Men had what they considered bad tidings to relate. Hunters had reported that a vast force of Kishoquoquilas were building a flight of stone steps in Stone Valley, from the foot of the Tussey Mountains to the summit.

Why this was being built was a mystery, except that it would enable the Kishoquoquilas Indians, in case they invaded the Northern Country, to cross the mountains with greater rapidity. They could make a "flying attack," as it were. Pipsisseway looked grave when he heard this. "Not only that," he said," but I believe those steps are being built because they feel certain they will conquer us after their invasion, and they want to minimize nature's barriers. After they imagine they have conquered us, they will expect to finish the steps down the northern slope of the mountain. Pipsisseway's abilities as a strategist were confirmed by spies whom he caused to be sent out. They returned, saying that Silver Eagle was assembling a vast army in the Southern valleys. He was drafting warriors from as far South as what is now Maryland and Virginia. From talk they had heard six or seven thousand braves were under arms. The purpose of the steps was now established. This vast force of Indians was at present spread out through the valleys. When the time arrived they could be marshaled quickly and sent across into Spruce Creek Valley on a run.

They would appear in this valley so suddenly that there would be no time to resist. Sweeping northward, they would pillage and capture everything in sight until they reached the royal encampment by the Susquehanna. The buildings would be burnt, Pipsisseway and his brothers surprised and murdered, while the beautiful Princess Meadow Sweet would be carried off to her old home in the South. Pipsisseway and his brothers dead, a marriage could be arranged between the young widow and Silver Eagle, who would rule over the largest domain on the eastern slope of the Alleghenies. The Indian Steps would be a recognized gateway of travel between the South and North. The most trustworthy and intelligent chiefs were summoned for conference with Pipsisseway and his Council. Fifty chieftains answered the call. It was decided by them that every male Indian fit for service should be moved in the direction of the Tussey Mountains. That was to be the ultimate destination, but they should tarry at all the frequented mountain passes where ingress from the South was afforded. But the rallying point was to be at the northern side of the "Indian Steps." Every brave was to start separately; no two men should travel together. It could not be said that a vast "body" of Indians was moving to the South; they would go as individuals. The chiefs returned to their homes, and ere long the advance began. Among them were Indians from the Chillesquaque country, led by Chief Hidden River; Indians from the Loyalsock region under Chief Mountain Ash; Indians from Nippenose Valley, led by Chief Lock-and-Bar; Indians from the region north of the royal encampment, in what is now Wayne Township, Clinton County, led by Chief Hazelwood; Indians from the Monsey Town Flats, as the country around what is now Lock Haven was called, commanded by Chief Gold Thread; Indians from the Sinnemahoning region, led by Chief Sonicle; Indians from the Bald Eagle Valley, under Chief Mountain Lion; Indians from Penn's Valley, led by Chief Panther Fangs, the grandfather, by the way, of the celebrated Indian Red Panther; Indians from the Black Forest, famed for their skill with bow and arrow and spear, led by Chief Tiadaghton; the Indians residing in Spruce Creek Valley, under Chief Golden Hour; all moving in a common direction by different routes, each as an individual, silent, loyal, determined. It was a subject of some discussion among Pipsisseway and his brothers if Meadow Sweet be allowed to accompany them. She pleaded so hard, and Pipsisseway relied so much on her judgment, that she went with the royal party. This consisted of King Pipsisseway, his brothers, the Council of Fifty Wise Men, the royal bodyguard, and household. Queen Meadow Sweet was attended by a single maiden. The rest of her retinue remained in the beautiful retreat by the Susquehanna, watched by one hundred picked Indians of the home-guard. The regal campground looked deserted when they were gone; it seemed a pity to leave such an ideal spot. Arriving in the Southern country the various tribesmen of the Susquehanahs camped out as individuals and waited. Spies who visited Stone Valley and adjoining valleys under cover of darkness reported that the main bodies of the Southern Indians, or Kishoquoquilas, were camping along what are now known as Shaver's Run, Globe Run, and Garner's Run. This showed that the line of attack was to be by way of the Steps. It was to be the sudden rush of a vast horde of warriors, whose combined strength would sweep everything before. When this in- formation was thoroughly verified, the Indians that were posted near the various points of ingress to the Susquehanah kingdom were concentrated in Spruce Creek Valley. All were ordered to remain in the forests, and it would be impossible to have imagined army lurking at the foot of the Tussey Mountains.

Undoubtedly the Kishoquoquilas sent out spies, but not finding any connected bodies of warriors, would imagine that the ones they saw were hunters or fishermen. The Steps were completed in the early winter, and the invasion was expected to follow. The army of the defense was on the alert, but nothing seemed to happen. Days and weeks passed. The forests were banked with snow. The waiting force became restless, hungry, and unhappy. They begged to be allowed to visit their homes and help their families. Permission was granted in rotation, and when an Indian left on a week's furlough, another would return from his trip the same day. Evidently the Kishoquoquilas finally received some intimation that a strong force awaited them, and were trying tactics of delay in order to reduce the numbers of their enemies. Some day when the defense was disorganized they would sweep over the mountain and the domain of Pipsisseway would be theirs. But the same dissatisfaction which had reigned among the Susquehanahs broke out among the Kishoquoquilas. It was an outrage to keep them so long without sign of a battle. Being encamped in compact bodies it was impossible to grant furloughs wholesale. In consequence there were threats of mutiny and desertion from some of the warriors from below the Potomac. An advance must be made, or the force could not be held together, was the advice given repeatedly to Silver Eagle by his aides. He would try to show them that the longer it was postponed the better the chance of finding their adversaries scattered and unprepared. "Your great mistake, sire," said Dangleberry, one of his oldest warriors," was in assembling your force before the completion of the Steps. You should have waited until a year after they were finished; then you would have found our enemies completely off their guard." "It's too late now," replied Silver Eagle, ruefully; "we must do the best we can." The reports of dissatisfaction were so overwhelming that one snowy morning at daybreak the advance, at double quick, was ordered. The force, numbering some five thousand braves, trooped up the Steps, over the summit, and down the rough mountain sides, coming on the level at the plains. As they emerged into the open country a terrific fusillade of arrows, darts, and spears assailed them from the forests on either side. Some of the more mercenary quickly retreated into the woods and up the mountain, but the majority, goaded on by their chiefs, kept advancing across the plain. The casualties in Pickett's Charge at Gettysburg were trifles compared to the harvest of death in this invasion of Spruce Creek Valley by the Kishoquoquilas. Before they were halfway across the open space, panic began seizing the entire body, and they ran from side to side, under the merciless rain of arrows. Many dropped into the snow from sheer fright and lay as dead. It is related that the entire invading army did not shoot five hundred arrows.

They were overcome with terror too quickly. All they could do was stagger about, waiting to be killed. Out of the five thousand who appeared on the plains, scarcely a thousand leached the forest on the northern edge of it in safety. These, when they came face to face with their enemies, felt renewed courage, and drawing their knives and tomahawks fought desperately. In a few minutes a thousand hand to hand conflicts of the bloodiest character were in progress. Silver Eagle was one of those lucky enough to cross the plain safely, and fought with diabolical bravery. He hacked his way through a mass of Susquehanahs, swearing that he'd reach the headquarters of Pipsisseway, the location of which he seemed to know, if he had to kill a thousand tribesmen on the way. He probably slew a score of Indians before he was free to run forward unhampered. In the distance, through the spaces between the trunks of the giant white oaks, he could make out a substantial lodge house built of logs. It stood a hundred yards from the Rock Spring, the source of Spruce Creek. "That's Pipsisseway's house; I'll kill him, I'll kill him; Meadow Sweet will yet be mine!" As he neared the door he saw the beautiful Queen emerge, looking weary and anxious. He waved to her, roaring, "I've killed your cursed husband; fly with me and be mine," and redoubled his pace through the wet snow. Just then a powerful voice rang out, "Not so fast, ambitious king, not so fast; I'm far from dead." He looked around and beheld his arch-enemy, Pipsisseway. He had not time to raise his tomahawk, for the King of the Susquehanahs had punctuated his greeting by cleaving his skull. He fell in a limp mass in the slush, his brains spattering about like a fox's entrails. Silver Eagle being dead, Pipsisseway rushed back into the thick of the conflict, and helped dispatch some of the few remaining Kishoquoquilas.

The slaughter continued all day long, and when night fell it was safe to say that there wasn't a living Kishoquoquilas north of Tussey Mountains. Even those who had fallen, panic-stricken, in the snow on the plains were butchered later when they attempted to sneak away. The order went out, "Kill every Kishoquoquilas; take no prisoners." As Pipsisseway, reeking with blood, tramped back to his lodge-house that night his mind evolved a fiendish revenge on his enemies. "I'll have Silver Eagle's body thrown into the Rock Spring, and every other corpse of his followers of high rank that we can identify. Rock Spring is the source of Spruce Creek, and Spruce Creek flows into the Juniata, that runs through the richest territory of the Kishoquoquilas. The putrefying carcasses of their king and the pick of their warriors shall taint the water that they drink."

Next morning this scheme was put into effect; over a hundred scalped and mutilated corpses being dumped into the Spring. For a full year the Indians who lived at the mouth of the creek said that the water smelled rancid even there. It was deemed unwholesome, and for years the redmen had an idea it was not fit to drink.

But what was pollution then adds to its purity now. Just as sugar is strained through bones, the crystalline source at Rock Spring flows through bones, the bones of warriors which time has left unsullied, and bubbles into the bowl of the spring limpid and sweet as dew. After the great conflict, which was called "The Battle of the Indian Steps," the Kishoquoquilas went on the decline. They split up into small tribes, and were constantly at war with one another. Pipsisseway did not follow up his victory, but returned to his beautiful retreat by the Susquehanna, where he died the following autumn of chills and fever. Besides his widow he left a son, named War Bonnet, who ultimately came to rule over his possessions. The Susquehanah kingdom enjoyed marked prosperity for nearly a hundred years after the great battle, only falling into a state of civil war during the last years of the Seventeenth Century. King Merciless and King Golden Treasure were two rival rulers of a later date, whose factional fights did much to disrupt the old kingdom. It seemed a shame that the passing of the redmen should have practically obliterated the Story of the Indian Steps and the resultant battle. But it is only one of the many historical legends that are fading away.

III.

The Legends of Penn's Cave

After Princess Nittany and Nittany Mountain, and the Indian wars for possession of this area, the most fabled place in the region surrounding the Nittany Valley is Penn's Cave. Three legends explicitly mention Penn's Cave.

The first legend, and perhaps the most romantic and evocative by far, consists of only one paragraph found in another legend in this collection, the story of "The Indians' Twilight: The Story of Grandfather Pine," printed in Chapter V. According to that one paragraph, Penn's Cave was formed as a result of the un-consummate-able love affair between the planet Earth and the planet Venus, as a result of which Earth asked the Sky to send a lightning bolt to let his anguish out. This lightning bolt both formed the cave that is there now, and opened the stream of water known today as Penn's Creek, which originates at a spring at Penn's Cave. In recognition of this origin, the stream that gushes from Penn's Cave was called by the Indian's the Karoondinha, which means the "Stream of Neverending Love." This brief story is part of the story of Grandfather Pine because the latter was also an expression of the Earth's "pining" for the love of Venus.

The second legend in this section is the very first legend published by Henry W. Shoemaker in 1902. This is the official legend featured at Penn's Cave, where it is painted on a large sign at the entrance. This legend tells not of the Princess Nittany over whose burial mound (or over whose lover's burial mound) Nittany Mountain arose in a single night, but of another Indian princess who lived about three hundred years later, and who was named after the original Princess Nittany featured in Part I of this book. In this poignant story, the daughter of an Indian Chief near Big Spring in Bellefonte falls in love with a French trapper named Malachi Boyer.

The third legend in this section, "Riding His Pony," tells the story of a mural, a painting on the wall of Penn's Cave, about which reports once circulated, but which has since disappeared due to age.

The Love of the Planet Earth
for the Planet Venus

Long years ago, in the very earliest days of the world's history, the great earth spirit loved the evening star, but it was such an unusual and unnatural attachment, and so impossible of consummation that the despairing spirit wished to end the cycle of existence and pass into oblivion so as to forget his hopeless love. Accordingly, with a blast of lightning he opened his side and let his anguish flow away. The great gaping wound is what we of to-day call Penn's Cave, and the never ending stream of anguish is the wonderful shadowy Karoondinha, now renamed John Penn's Creek.

The Legend of Penn's Cave

As related by Isaac Steele, an Aged Seneca Indian, in 1892: In the days when the West Branch Valley was a trackless wilderness of defiant pines and submissive hemlocks twenty-five years before the first pioneer had attempted lodgment beyond Sunbury, a young Pennsylvania Frenchman, from Lancaster County, named Malachi Boyer, alone and unaided, pierced the jungle to a point where Bellefonte is now located.

The history of his travels has never been written, partly because he had no white companion to observe them, and partly because he himself was unable to write. His very identity would now be forgotten were it not for the traditions of the Indians, with whose lives he became strangely entangled.

A short, stockily built fellow was Malachi Boyer, with unusually prominent black eyes and black hair that hung in ribbon-like strands over his broad, low forehead. Fearless, yet conciliatory, he escaped a thousand times from Indian cunning and treachery, and as the months went by and he penetrated further into the forests he numbered many redskins among his cherished friends.

Why he explored these boundless wilds he could not explain, for it was not in the interest of science, as he scarcely knew of such a thing as geography, and it was not for trading, as he lived by the way. But on he forced his path, ever aloof from his own race, on the alert for the strange scenes that encompassed him day by day.

One beautiful month of April—there is no one who can tell the exact year—found Malachi Boyer camped on the shores of Spring Creek. Near the Mammoth Spring was an Indian camp, whose occupants maintained a quasi-intercourse with the pale-faced stranger. Sometimes old Chief O-ko cho would bring gifts of corn to Malachi, who in turn presented the chieftain with a hunting knife of truest steel. And in this way Malachi came to spend more and more of his time about the Indian camps, only keeping his distance at night and during religious ceremonies.

Old O-ko-cho's chief pride was centered in his seven stalwart sons, Hum-kin, Ho-ko-lin, Too-chin, Os-tin, Chaw-kee-bin, Aha-kin, Ko-lo-pa-kin and his Diana-like daughter, Nita-nee. The seven brothers resolved themselves into a guard of honor for their sister, who had many suitors, among whom was the young chief E-Faw, from the adjoining sub-tribe of the A-caw-ko-tahs. But Nita-nee gently, though firmly, repulsed her numerous suitors, until such time as her father would' give her in marriage to one worthy of her regal blood.

Thus ran the course of Indian life when Malachi Boyer made his bed of hemlock boughs by the gurgling waters of Spring Creek. And it was the first sight of her, washing a deer-skin in the stream, that led him to prolong his stay and ingratiate himself with her father's tribe.

Few were the words that passed between Malachi and Nita-nee, many the glances, and often did the handsome pair meet in the mossy ravines near the camp grounds. But this was all clandestine love, for friendly as Indian and white might be in social intercourse, never could a marriage be tolerated, until— there always is a turning point in romance—the black-haired wanderer and the beautiful Nita-nee resolved to spend their lives together, and one moonless night started for the more habitable East. All night long they threaded their silent way, climbing down mountain ridges, gliding through the velvet-soiled hemlock glades, and wading, hand in hand, the splashing, resolute torrents. When morning came they breakfasted on dried meat and huckleberries, and bathed their faces in a mineral spring. Until—there is always a turning point in romance—seven tall, stealthy forms, like animated mountain pines, stepped from the gloom and surrounded the eloping couple. Malachi drew a hunting knife, identical with the one he had given to Chief O-ko-cho, and, seizing Nita-nee around the waist, stabbed right and left at his would-be captors.

The first stroke pierced Hum-kin's heart, and, uncomplainingly, he sank down dying. The six remaining brothers, although receiving stab wounds, caught Malachi in their combined grasp and disarmed him; then one brother held sobbing Nita-nee, while the others dragged fighting Malachi across the mountain.

That was the last the lovers saw of one another. Below the mountain lay a broad valley, from the center of which rose a circular hillock, and' it was to this mound the savage brothers led their victim. As they approached, a yawning cavern met their eyes, filled with greenish limestone water. There is a ledge at the mouth of the cave, about six feet higher than the water, above which the arched roof rises thirty feet, and it was from here they shoved Malachi Boyer into the tide below. He sank for a moment, but when he rose to the surface, commenced to swim. He approached the ledge, but the brothers beat him back, so he turned and made for some dry land in the rear of the cavern. Two of the brothers ran from the entrance over the ridge to watch, where there is another small opening, but though Malachi tried his best, in the impenetrable darkness, he could not find this or any other avenue of escape. He swam back to the cave's mouth, but the merciless Indians were still on guard. He climbed up again and again, but was repulsed, and once more retired to the dry cave. Every day for a week he renewed his efforts to escape, but the brothers were never absent. Hunger became unbearable, his strength gave way, but he vowed he would not let the redskins see him die, so, forcing himself into one of the furthermost labyrinths, Malachi Boyer breathed his last.

Two days afterward the brothers entered the cave and discovered the body. They touched not the coins in his pockets, but weighted him with stones and dropped him into the deepest part of the greenish Limestone water. And after these years those who have heard this legend declare that on the still summer nights an unaccountable echo rings through the cave, which sounds like "Nita-nee," "Nita-nee."

Riding His Pony

When Rev. James Martin visited the celebrated Penn's Cave, in the Spring of 1795, it was related that he found a small group of Indians encamped there. That evening, around the campfire, one of the redskins related a legend of one of the curiosities of the watery cave, the flambuoyant "Indian Riding Pony" mural-piece which decorates one of the walls.

Spirited as a Remington, it bursts upon the view, creates a lasting impression, then vanishes as the power skiff, the "Nita-nee," draws nearer.

According to the old Indians, there lived not far from where the Karoondinha emerges from the cavern a body of aborigines of the Susquehannock tribe who made this delightful lowland their permanent abode. While most of their cabins were huddled near together on the upper reaches of the stream, there were straggling huts clear to the Beaver Dams. The finding of arrow points, beads and pottery along the creek amply attests to this.

Among the clan was a maiden named Quetajaku, not good to look upon, but in no way ugly or deformed. In her youth she was light-hearted and sociable, with a gentle disposition. Yet for some reason she was not favored by the young bucks. All her contemporaries found lovers and husbands, but poor Quetajaku was left severely alone. She knew that she was not beautiful, though she was of good size; she was equally certain that she was not a physical monster. She could not understand why she could find no lover, why she was singled out to be a "chauchschisis," or old maid.

It hurt her pride as a young girl, it broke her heart completely when she was older.

Gradually she withdrew from the society of her tribal friends, building herself a lodge-house on the hill, in what is now the cave orchard. There she led a very introspective life, grieving over the love that might have been. To console herself she imagined that some day a handsome warrior would appear, seek her out, load her with gifts, overwhelm her with love and carry her away to some distant region in triumph. He would be handsomer and braver than any youth in the whole country of the Karoondinha. She would be the most envied of women when he came.

This poor little fancy saved her from going stark mad; it remedied the horror of her lonely lot. Every time the night wind stirred the rude hempen curtain which hung before the door of her cabin, she would picture it was the chivalrous stranger knight come to claim her. When it was cold she drew the folds of her buffalo robe tighter about her as if it was his arms.

As time went on she grew happy in her secret lover, whom no other woman's flame could equal, whom no one could steal away. She was ever imagining him saying to her that her looks exactly suited him, that she was his ideal.

But like the seeker after Eldorado, years passed, and Quetajaku did not come nearer to her spirit lover. But her soul kept up the conceit; every night when she curled herself up to sleep he was the vastness of the night.

On one occasion an Indian artist named Naganit, an undersized old wanderer appeared at the lonely woman's home. For a living he decorated pottery, shells and bones, sometimes even painted war pictures on rocks. Quetajaku was so kind to him that he built himself a lean-to on the slope of the hill, intending to spend the winter.

On the long winter evenings the old woman confided to the wanderer the story of her unhappy life, of her inward consolation. She said that she had longed to meet an artist who could carry out a certain part of her dream which had a right to come true.

When she died she had arranged to be buried in a fissure of rocks which ran horizontally into one of the walls of the "watery" cave. On the opposite wall she would like painted in the most brilliant colors a portrait of a handsome young warrior, with arms outstretched, coming towards her.

Naganit said that he understood what she meant exactly, but suggested that the youth be mounted on a pony, a beast which was coming into use as a mount for warriors, of which he had lately seen a number in his travels on the Virginia coast, near Chincoteague.

This idea was pleasing to Quetajaku, who authorized the stranger to begin work at once. She had saved up a little property of various kinds; she promised to bestow all of this on Naganit, except what would be necessary to bury her, if the picture proved satisfactory.

The artist rigged up a dog-raft with a scaffold on it, and this he poled into the place where the fissure was located, the woman accompanying him the first time, so there would be no mistake. All winter long by torchlight, he labored away. He used only one color, an intensive brick-red made from mixing sumac berries, the pollen of the Turk's Cap Lily, a small root and the bark of a tree, as being more permanent than that made from ochers and other ores of stained earth.

Marvelous and vital was the result of this early impressionist; the painting had all the action of life. The superb youth in war dress, with arms outstretched, on the agile war pony, rushing towards the foreground, almost in the act of leaping from the rocky panel into life, across the waters of the cave to the arms of his beloved.

It would make old Quetajaku happy to see it, she who had never known love or beauty. The youth in the mural typified what Naganit would have been himself were he the chosen, and what the "bachelor maid" would have possessed had nature favored her. It was the ideal for two disappointed souls.

Breathlessly the old artist ferried Quetajaku to the scene of his endeavors. When they reached the proper spot he held aloft his quavering torch. Quetajaku, in order to see more clearly, held her two hands above her eyes. She gave a little cry of exclamation, then turned and looked at Naganit intently. Then she dropped her eyes, beginning to cry to herself, a rare thing for an Indian to do!

The artist looked at her fine face, down which the tears were streaming, and asked her the cause of her grief—was the picture such a terrible disappointment?

The woman drew herself together, replying that it was grander than she had anticipated, but the face of Niganit's, and, strangely enough, the face she had dreamed of all her life.

"But I am not the heroic youth you pictured", said the artist, sadly. "I am sixty years old, stoop-shouldered, and one leg is shorter than the other."

"But that is how you would look on your war pony; it is your face, shoulders and arms. You are the picture that I always hoped would come true."

Niganit looked at the Indian woman. She was not hideous; there was even a dignity to her large, plain features, her great, gaunt form.

"I have never received such praise as yours. I always vowed I would love the woman who really understood me and my art. I am yours. Let us think no more of funeral decorations, but go to the east, to the land of war ponies, and ride to endless joy together."

Quetajaku, overcome by the majesty of his words, leaned against his massive shoulder. In that way he poled his dog-raft against the current to the entrance of the cave. There was a glory in the reflection from the setting sun over against the east; night, would not close in for an hour or two. And towards the darkening east that night two happy travelers could be seen wending their way.

IV.
How the Indians Became Braves

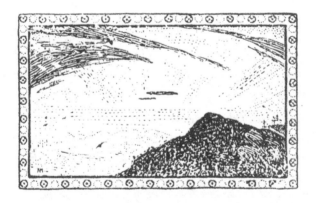

Of all the legends and tales of the Indians, the following is by far the editor's favorite. It presents, in the most sublime story-form, the challenge of how to instill courage in people. No one who studies the Indians of North America comes away without admiration for their bravery; indeed, to this day while European fighters are usual-

ly referred to as simply soldiers, Indian fighters are almost always called "Braves."

In this legend, Shoemaker explains why this difference occurs: "The Christian Bible," he writes, "tells the origin of sin, the Indian legends repeat the beginnings of valor. The Indians never acknowledged that they sinned, perhaps they never did; the people of the Bible never laid stress on their bravery."

In this story, the Great Gitchie Manitou becomes bored with the creatures he had created, because everything had been given to them without needing any effort on their part. So, Gitchie Manitou calls forth the monstrous serpent of the underworld, the great Machtando to tear apart the surface of the earth, destroying the basis of the red men's effortless existence; they are forced to confront the greatest evil and overcome it or cease to live.

A young, unnamed hero is found to teach them courage. For the first time they must learn the meaning of the words "brave," "belief," and "divine." He orders a huge spear to be built to thrust into the neck of the serpent when it comes out of the ground. To guide and push it into place, however, the Indians must summon superhuman courage.

At the end of the battle, the unnamed hero gives thanks saying "It is not for the death of the worst foe that could attack us we wish to give thanks, it is for the birth of our souls, of our new valor, of our hope for immortality." He reminds them to never forget the symbol of this first act of courage: "Let none of you forget the spear," he tells them.

"And so it came to pass that Indians always carried spears when on the chase or in battle," recounts the legend.

Yet, Shoemaker notes at the end of the story that both the early settlers, and later historians viewing drawings or paintings of the

Indians encountered, have long wondered at the "apparent useless-ness of the weapons" that they saw the Indians carrying. The legend helps explain that the light, flimsy spears they habitually carried were not so much carried as serious weapons, but as symbols—"they were the armament of the red men's souls," the legend explains, con-stant reminders of the "greatest feat of the red man's existence"—when the Indians earned the right to be called Braves.

And all this happened, according to legend, at the end of the Bald Eagle mountain range that runs along the western side of State College, parallel to the Nittany Mountain range to the east, in be-tween which lies the beautiful Nittany Valley.

The Birth of the Bald Eagles

In the earliest day that Indian myth and folk-lore have knowledge of, the region which we now call Central Pennsylvania was a flat and fertile plain, interspersed with clumps of rich tropical-like trees and bubbling springs, and where grazed countless herds of strange looking animals and reptiles, ancestral types of those found there upon the advent of the white men. Sometimes the bunches of luxuriant trees grew out of hillocks or knobs, and on these the savage forerunners of the Indian tribes had their abodes. They had come so lately from the bosom of Gitchie-Manitto the Almighty, for the world was new, and had experienced so few of the vicissitudes now so inherent to the generations, that if they had religious belief, it would be founded on a certainty. Things had not run contrary to their wishes, consequently they had not found the advisability to inquire into their beginnings.

Fruits of all kinds, as well as nuts and cereals grew at hand in abundance. A new taste, for the flesh of animals, birds and fishes had sharpened their appetites. All was easy, opulent, serene. They were beloved by their Great First Cause and grew comfortable and complacent in the very radiance of His blessing.

Wars, quarrels, strife, competition, all the emulative features of life, were lacking in their composition—their backbones had not hardened. One hour of modern life with its upsets, backsets and rivalries, would have exhausted their untried energies. They lacked the motive force to send a line of hardy descendants down the ages. They had not demonstrated their rights for existence.

But they were fearless, in a sense, although nothing had ever happened to make them afraid. In plain words they were spiritually "half-baked." There must be reasons why humanity was made what it is. The Christian Bible tells the origin of sin, the Indian legends repeat the beginnings of valor. The Indians never acknowledged that they sinned, perhaps they never did; the people of the Bible never laid stress on their bravery. But it was to be the fate of the Indians that they carne down the ages physically and spiritually brave and only by contamination with the whites did their deterioration begin. But for centuries they lived in the broad plains of Central Pennsylvania, no better nor worse, than when the Great Spirit breathed His breath into the clay; their inertia must have begun to pall on Him. Only men of action have immortal souls, the Indians had none in those days there are no Indian ghosts dating from remote antiquity nor are there legends of any. Perhaps their lack of individuality and progress were all a part of the deeply laid plans of the Great Spirit.

Valor, to be the dominant trait of the Indian character, was not to be developed until they were physically fit. But when time had produced a magnificent race of beings their testing out process was to begin. Like all acts of the Great Spirit it came about in a way that could not be long foretold.

It occurred after a season of unparalleled calmness and prosperity, in a joyous, bracing autumn, when the redmen smelt the falling leaves, and it was too cool to doze in the half-crisp, half-sultry sunshine. It came first in the form of news from Indians whose canoes had started far towards the head-waters of Bald Eagle Creek, and like tawny Paul Reveres brought the message of a new order of things, to their peaceful, indifferent fellows in the land of the Susquehanna. And once they heard it, not an Indian rested as calmly as of yore. The bearers of tidings told of a vast upheaval of the earth, moving irresistibly eastward, like the progress of some monstrous mole. Where once were smooth plains, covered with groves of oaks and pine or giant ferns, or fields waving with Indian corn, were now great mountainous masses of broken rocks rifted from the centers of the earth. Springs and water-courses were loosed from their rocky fastnesses, and gushed forth in torrents through the crevices in this new formed face of nature. A force that from within could raise such huge mountains, some of them a thousand feet in height, must be titanic in its strength and immensity, almost a creator of worlds itself.

Death and destruction had followed this birth of a mountain range. The peaceful redmen would fall asleep one night in their cool tents, along some stream on the rich plains, never dreaming of aught but plenty and contentment. During the night the earth beneath them would rise, sometimes quickly, other times unsteadily, as if some vast monster was turning in his slumbers. Tents, lodges, campfires, Indians old and young, would be hurled to their deaths, or sink to burial alive in the new-formed crannies and abysses. The sun would rise from behind a rocky peak instead of gliding gracefully into vision above the horizon. The sound of happy voices was no more, only the dull, ominous rumble of the great masses of rock, earth, and uprooted timber settling into place. And this horror was moving steadily eastward, forming a new mountain sometimes every night. As it seemed endless in its course, the Indians dwelling further east, moved rapidly from the radius of the new development, but some were caught unawares when side ridges, mostly to the south, were suddenly heaved from the plains. The far-eastern Indians heard the news with dismay; it was either combat the oncoming force, or fly before it. But what good was flight, if mountains shot up in every nook of safety. But how to combat it was the question. All the physical force of every Indian on the vast American continent rolled together could not stay a force vast enough to heave up mountains from the plains. It was futile to concoct schemes to combat it, human energy was nil. It had not occurred that a supernatural power could be invoked. The Indians of those ancient simple days were much like our white people in this modern complex age, they did not know how to pray or who to pray to. They accepted everything as a matter of course, they had a physical name for every ghost.

They called the rain, when it pattered on the birch-bark roof of the lodge-house, just rain, it was not the footsteps of a wraith. They called the wind, when it howled dismally through the pine woods, or swept shrieking up the open bed of the river, just wind, and not a disembodied, unhappy spirit calling for surcease. They called the shadows, when they fell suddenly in front of a traveller's path, or hid the surroundings of a peaceful camp, just shadows, and not the dimly seen presence of a ghost or troop of ghosts. They called the sighing splash of distant waterfalls, just waterfalls, and not the song of the banshee or "token." The crackling of boughs, or the sudden fall of a tree at night in the forest, was just nature, and not unseen hands working out their purposes.

It was a very prosaic world of facts, much like the world we live in now. We have as many ghosts about us today as we had a hundred years ago, but like the Indians of old, we have given them physical names. But they are ghosts all the same; some day they will come to their own. But this complete understanding of this world as a purely physical manifestation had its limitations. When human agency failed there was nothing that drew out the reserve force. In a world where there are ghosts, the big deeds of valor and unselfish bravery are accomplished. A prayerful world is a hopeful, undaunted world. And yet these simple aborigines differed in one great fundamental principle from our modern materialists. The Indians were creedless, but cheerful; they did not have the pessimistic gloom of modern faithlessness. We bemoan a faith once held, but thrown away; they were comfortable because they cared for nothing before or behind. But in this crisis, when the onrush of a nascent range of mountains daily grew more imminent, physical opposition being footless, they must needs appeal from it somehow. Among their number they acknowledged one man wiser than the rest, yet he was only a very young man. Of course his name is lost in the shrouds of time, but a name matters very little where there is accomplishment; it is only useful with society people who do nothing, and need a name to prop them a brief period on the ragged edge of the inevitable oblivion. Without striving, this young man had been by common consent acknowledged to be the superior of all others.

Distinctions of birth were unknown in those days, but his wisdom made him king, and he became the progenitor of descendants growing less wise with each generation until at the time of the white men's invasion, they were the dullest of their tribes.

This wise man, when they appealed to him for some recourse other than flight and to stop the destruction of their happy lands, said he must go out to the barest part of the plains, to meditate for seven or eight days. He went, taking scanty provisions to ensure high thinking, but was back after one night's solitude. He told them, when they assembled before him, that their desire to remain where they were was an inspiration, nothing less, but furthermore, if they were brave and believed, they could forever stop the onslaught of their destroyer, who was mighty but not divine.

His speech was intelligible, except for the words "brave," "belief," "divine." They dealt with a range of experience beyond their orbit. The wise man seeing this, explained them as best he could, and to the credit of the redmen let it be said they understood.

With this much gained, he proceeded to tell them of the secret of their birth, something they had not known nor cared about before. After once they heard it they were different beings, it was as if a divine spark from the realm where it abounds, had penetrated them; they never felt the same again. The Great First Cause, who made them ("but who made the Great First Cause" was their unanimous demand, and this remained unanswered) desired to instill a new virtue, courage, into the supine, calm dwellers on the plains. He had permitted a Machtando or giant monster of the underworld, whose home had been many leagues toward the centre of the earth, to disport himself mole-like beneath the outer lining of the globe.

Nature is wasteful of its seed, except when it has some purpose to conserve, and the lives blotted out in the monster's track were uncounted and would have availed not. But the vast body of dwellers, to the eastward, who had learned of the great changes, were to be given a chance to save themselves, and make themselves in the full sense, Men.

But here the concourse again interrupted the wise man. "Who made the Great First Cause?" they clamored. "That will be answered some day to each of you," said the speaker calmly, "you will laugh that you were ever dumb enough to ask such a question, it will be so simple". At any rate, the Indians were to win their birthright, only to lose it to a race ages later, with a purer faith than theirs. Four moons from the time of the assemblage, the monster mountain builder was due to emerge, head first, from his chain of hills. The place chosen by him was to be on the fertile, thickly populated plains, across the swelling river from what the Indians afterwards called Molisey or Muncy Town.

If the redmen defeated and destroyed the monster, they would increase, multiply and prosper; if they failed, all would meet the fate of their compatriots to the west, not one but a horde of similar monsters would rise out of the earth and annihilate them. The Indians could conquer, if they would be brave, and bravery was synonymous with belief. Believing in oneself is equivalent to a creed, for God, or the Great First Cause, we all know is within us, to a greater or lesser extent. God is the power within us to do things. During the time intervening until the great monster shoved forth his Gorgon's head, the Indians were to prepare his doom. First of all they were to shape a huge granite rock, which lay (perhaps put there by divine foresight, on the river bank) into a spear point. This they were to smear thickly with poisons which could be dug from the earth, the wise man would show them where. Then they were to fasten the spear point to a handle made from many tree trunks laid side by side, fastened by hickory poles, and securely spliced at the ends.

All this was to be raised from the ground on trucks or wheels, made from smooth beech logs, and at the sides propelled by every Indian able to navigate. The logs were to be indented for each Indian's body, and his full force would help send it forward. The wise man showed them the place where the monster would emerge, and where to station their poisoned ram. When they heard the ripping of roots, the cracking of boulders, and the bursting of soil, denoting the appearance of the menace, they would get ready to set the instrument of defense into motion. When the huge head, open-fanged, emerged, they were, by concerted effort, to drive the sharpened, poisoned end down its venomous throat.

The wise man had tried to make himself clear; there was little more to say. Before dismissing the concourse, however, he bade them recite after him a short prayer to the Great First Cause, because that was the only part of his discourse they had not understood. Self-preservation came naturally enough, but the idealistic part, the power not seen, yet themselves solely, was too abstract, too far from immediate benefits to shape itself succinctly in their plant-like intellects.

But they followed him word for word, and reverently, in the prayer. Before the mood for action would change, the young soothsayer led his people to the great flat rock, and set them to drilling one end to a point.

Buoyed up by their new ideals they worked faster and more skillfully than even their leader deemed it possible. Despite their vast numbers, not one worker conflicted with another; it was inspired team work. While they were pounding away, the wise man selected the trees which were to form the trucks or handle to the giant war-spear.

These being chosen, and marked, he set the enthusiastic workers constructing it, as soon as the spear-head was done to his satisfaction. They say that after four days and nights of cheerful labor, the great weapon was ready to be hurled against the foe.

Meanwhile the old men, and the women and children were moved far to the eastward, and settled comfortably amid hills and valleys, until the conflict should be over. So confident was the wise man of the ultimate triumph that he forbid families at parting to say goodbye, he determined to make faith of victory certain. He drilled the force who were to operate the ram, until they handled the mighty weapon dexterously. Then there was nothing to do but to wait developments. The foe might not appear for four moons, but there was a danger of its appearance sooner. They did not have to wait until they became tired or disorganized. It was not long until they heard the awful rumble of mountains in the making. The ground shook where they were encamped, as if mammoths were disporting themselves under their very feet. One clear haze-less morning they beheld the great circular outlines of a mountain, looming against the horizon, seven or eight miles to the westward, where the night before none had been.

The "mountain builder" was almost upon them; at this rate, their conflict with him, would occur that night or the next morning. In order to let them see plainly by night, the wise man ordered the plains and forests fired. When the sun sank miles of blazing grass and tree ferns illuminated the scene with a lurid, uncanny glow. All had been silent since the morning, the monster had evidently retired below, to rest before another effort. At midnight they heard a tremendous crunching of rocks and roots, the signal that the mountain building had begun afresh. Some of the Indians almost went mad from the deafening roar, so sustained, so loud, so nerve-racking. It reached a pitch where it overpowered everything, and the tensely strained ear drums became used to it. But many of the redmen were totally deafened for life. By the orange-red glare of the burning vegetation, they noted the level of the plain rising higher and higher. The work of upheaval had begun right before them; it was their chance now to stop the hideous monster, and earn a patrimony of valor to send on to generations yet unborn. Amid the terrific noises, the back-bone of a mountain rose into view, a mountain a mile in width and close to a thousand feet in height.

As it was settling into a permanent contour, they noticed a rending in the structure of its easterly slope; the monster, evidently apprised of his human enemies, was preparing to issue forth to give them battle. Soon the vast horned-head of the Machtando, or demon, did emerge, shooting forth gaseous vapors so foul, that it sickened many of the defenders. But those who could overcome their indisposition, manned the ram bravely, and sent it in motion after the fiendish monster. Both head and ram moved with about the same acceleration, and force. But the Indians were gifted on that occasion with superhuman courage, and drove the sharpened spear point into the open maw of the on-coming foe. For an instant all seemed swallowed in the mass of sulphurous smoke, but the sharpened apex went true, coming out the back of the monster's neck. Transfixed it could move neither forward nor backward, but its subterranean body lashed itself wildly, sending fresh convulsions through the newly formed mountain. Sooner or later the creature might have freed himself, but for the poison, so liberally smeared over the spearhead. Before he could devise a way to shake off his enemies, he was in the throes of a horrible death-agony. Struggling with might and main, he was forcing the blade out of his jaws, when the chilling forces of death overcame him. But he did not become still until after the entire form had turned itself completely over, causing that noticeable breadth at the termination of what we now style Muncy Mountain.

When he had gasped for the last time, like some foundry blowing off, and lay like the heights above, perfectly still, the wise man clambered out on the truck of the weapon, and asked the prayers of the valiant band. "It is not for the death of the worst foe that could attack us we wish to give thanks, it is for the birth of our souls, of our new valor, of our hope for immortality." The Indians, for the most part utterly exhausted, fell on the earth, uttering grateful expressions.

They had won a notable and lasting victory. "Let none of you forget the spear" said the wise man when he bade them disperse. And so it came to pass that Indians always carried spears when on the chase or in battle.

Antiquarians have wondered at the apparent uselessness of these weapons, but they were the armament of the redmen's souls, the symbol of the grandest feat of their existence. When they carried them it augured something great. And the mountain range which came into being was called the Machtando, or Devil Mountains, until rechristened centuries later in honor of the great Chief Bald Eagle.

V.
The Passing Away
of the Pennsylvania Indians

*No question or issue was felt more keenly by the early gatherers
of the oral histories of the Indians who once populated North Ameri-*

ca than their approaching fate to be driven from their lands to almost complete extinction.

Probably no legend or story of all the Indian lore ever collected more poignantly reminds us of this fate than the first legend included below, in which Shoemaker records the origin of Indian summer.

After reading this story, you will never again be able to enjoy a beautiful sunny day in late October, or feel a warm breeze across your face in mid-November—the season of "Indian Summer"—without recalling the sad fate of the Indian peoples who lived in these hills and valleys before us, and vanished at our coming. For that remembrance, according to this legend, is the meaning of this special season: to forever remind us at least once each year of the good, beautiful, and brave people who were here before the settlers arrived.

The second legend in this section, "The Indians' Twilight: The Story of Grandfather Pine," is one of the most fertile and fecund of all the stories in this collection, for it gives rein to imagine more connections and relations between the divine and supernatural, and our daily lives, than almost any other.

Actually, it is five legends in one.

First, it is the legend of the love felt by the planet Earth for the planet Venus, resulting in the Earth asking the Sky to send forth a lightning bolt to release the anguish of love felt by the Earth over the impossibility of ever consummating this love because of the astronomical distance between Venus and Earth. In response to Earth's request the Sky sends forth a lightning bolt that gashes the Earth, forming the cave that comes to be known as Penn's Cave. This portion—but a single paragraph—of "The Indians' Twilight: The Story of Grandfather Pine" is excerpted above as one of the legends about Penn's Cave.

The same lightning bolt also releases the Earth's anguish by creating the spring that is the source of what the local Indian tribes named the Karoondinha, which means the "Stream of the Neverending Love" (or "anguish" at impossible love), and which the settlers renamed John Penn's Creek.

Thus this legend not only tells us the mystical origin of Penn's Cave, but also the mystical origin and romantic meaning of Penn's Creek. No young man whose heart is broken as the result of a lost love will ever again be able to see Venus in the evening sky without thinking of this legend. Similarly, no one who ever visits, hikes along, or takes a canoe or raft down the waters of Penn's Creek will ever forget where and why this stream originates—from a spring created along with Penn's Cave by a lightning bolt, from which flows the lover's anguish of the Earth.

The third and most tantalizing part of this legend deals with the origin of Grandfather Pine. This is the story of why such a tall tree (an astounding 276 feet tall according witnesses quoted in the story) came to grow so tall in the first place. It was because it was another manifestation of the Earth's love for Venus; modern psychologists might well call it the story of the largest phallic symbol ever told.

The fourth part of this legend deals with the fact that, because of its origin, the Grandfather Pine became the most sacred meeting place for all the Indian tribes of Pennsylvania (and perhaps of all the tribes of the northeastern United States) when decisions affecting the fate of all Indians were to be decided.

Finally, the fifth part of this legend deals with a particular assembly in historic times of all the tribes to discuss what to do in the face of the encroachments of the settlers. Historians have long been puzzled by the lack of effective resistance by the Indians of the northeast. According to this legend, it was not for lack of courage, but by the will of the Great Gitchie Manitou that all the best warriors, chiefs, and medicine men were called to climb up the Grandfather Pine and enter the heavens to hold council with Gitchie Manitou. Apparently, the Gitchie Manitou did not want them to resist the expanding settlements, for they never came down, thus leaving Indian lands open and defenseless against the invasion of the Europeans. Historically, therefore, this legend offers a mystical explanation for the course of the Indian wars against the settlers in Pennsylvania, and why the settlers so easily won.

But it leaves open the possibility that all those warriors and chiefs and medicine men are still up there. Perhaps the Gitchie Manitou has plans for them to come back to accomplish something very great—when they are truly needed.

I was always told as a boy that the Indians believed that the stars in the sky were the campfires of Braves who, when they died, went to the Great Beyond. But now I cannot look at the star studded night sky without imagining that the stars are the campfires of all those Braves called by the Gitchie Manitou to climb the Grandfather Pine, and wondering for what great purpose the Gitchie Manitou has been saving them—and when they will come back, presumably to save the Earth when it faces its greatest need...

The Glory of Indian Summer

Many persons have wondered what was the origin of the words "Indian Summer." Only recently a correspondent wrote to the New York Evening Sun, asking for this information. But the paper usually so explicit did not give a very definite reply, except that it was first known in written language in 1794. The Lenni-Lenape used to say that Indian Summer was more properly the name of a girl, though it was also the name of a season. Lena-kit-chita was the name of the Indian maid, and it also corresponded with the word meaning this most delightful period of the year.

Five or six centuries ago there was a notable encampment of Indians on the slopes of Mount Eagle, in the Bald Eagle range. At that time this region was a stronghold of the now vanished Lenni-Lenape. This picturesque and valiant tribe had a particularly courageous chief called Chau-wa-lanne, or Forked-Tail Eagle, whose personal bravery and charm had much to do with cementing the clans into closer union. He maintained his regal lodge-house on the summit of Mount Eagle; believing that he was descended from the king of birds, and must live as in an eyrie. The remainder of the settlement was upon the lower levels of the mountains and in the ravine below. It has come down to us that over fifteen hundred souls made up its quota. Five hundred of these were trained warriors, the pick of the tribal organizations. There was not one of them who stood under six feet in height; they were an "old guard" of an earlier day. Chau-wa-lanne himself was taller than any of his warriors, with that keen eye beneath busy brows, and sharp curved nose, so characteristic of stout-hearted men. Though very tall, he was willowy and graceful; he could outjump any member of his tribe, he could outrun the swiftest deer. In the chase he always outran his game; he considered it beneath his dignity to stand still and shoot.

An eagle flies above its prey until it falls exhausted and is overcome easily, and this was precisely the method of Chau-wa-lanne. Once he chased a giant panther through the forest, up trees, and down again, leaping from one rock to another, crawling over ravines on grape-vines and prostrate logs, but he tired the animal, and broke its jaw with his iron hand, without a struggle. Struck with pity for the magnificent brute, he dragged him back to his lodge and made him a pet. The animal was readily tamed, and made an admirable "watch-dog."

There was a giant forked white pine near the lodge-house, its spiral, buck-topped pinnacles seemed to unite with the heavenly dome. Two pairs of eagles made their nests in the cage-like tops, emblems of perpetual good luck to Chau-wa-lanne, living beneath. In every way he seemed to be one of the chosen of Gitchie-Manitto, the Great Spirit.

It does seem as if some souls are selected to do the big work in this life. All is so easy to them, every wish so quickly gratified. With others it is a painful struggle, a long siege of dis-appointment, unappreciation, uncongenial tasks. It is a case of striving only to be beaten back until one sinks into the inactivity of despair. The Great Spirit has cast such to play minor roles. But with Chau-wa-lanne to wish was to realize; life is a success to the divinely anointed. But unlike a few of Infinity's favorites, he did not become vain and overbearing. The sharp, keen outlines of his dominant face showed that enervation, the indolence of happiness, could never be his. His was a warrior's part, a mountaineer's part, a hunter's part, the attributes of his fanciful eagle-blood. His father, Wiponquoak, or White Oak, a noted chief before him had died a lingering death from wounds received in one of his victorious battles when Chau-wa-lanne was only nineteen; responsibility coming upon him at this early age helped to develop his Spartan qualities. But like Alexander he longed for fresh worlds to conquer, he longed to incite warfare in distant tribes.

But none would provoke this human tower of strength. At twenty-four he was like some great pinioned bird, seeking to unfold wings designed to rule the high air.

It was at this mentally mature period of his life that love was born. Always a hunter and a soldier, a man's man, his romances had been few and far between. Furthermore he was so beautiful physically, his ways so engaging, that a nod would have brought any woman to his side, even if he had not been a king. When love settled down like a dove in an eagle's nest, it was for the beautiful maiden Lena-kit-chita, or Indian Summer, daughter of the famous captain Woakus or Grey Fox. By birth she was not the equal of Chau-wa-lanne, few would have been for that matter, but her blood was noble, of the rank of many noted chiefs and warriors, even if she could not claim kinship with Chau-wa-lanne. Caste was firmly adhered to in those days; the Indians saw the evils of misalliances much more intelligently than we of today with all our ancestral societies and heraldic manifestations. It was generally the custom for an Indian King to marry a woman who was related to him, to "keep the rank in the family," but there was no positive barrier against a union with an unrelated person provided she was of noble blood. Lena-kit-chita being well born, and the most beautiful of her tribe, could not be discriminated against; the loyal subjects rejoiced at their beloved monarch's decision to take a wife who might send his seed down the ages. It was a genuine love match, at least after all these years tradition declares that it was, although there had been an earlier lover in the life of Lena-kit-chita. There was no doubt but that it was Chau-wa-lanne's first affair.

An Indian could not burst the bonds of caste through being a warrior or a hunter, no matter how superlatively brave he might be, or if he was a weapon-maker or artist, but if he possessed the gift of second sight, was a wise man, he could raise his social status next to that of the king. There was a poor widow in the camp, her husband in his lifetime had trapped pigeons, making coats out of the sunrise-colored breasts of the male birds, in other words was an Indian draper.

This aged woman had one son, whose spiritual gifts had made him the most noted man in the settlement. They called him Wili-wili-han, or the soothsayer. Despite the fact that mentally he towered above every Indian of his tribe, physically he was at a disadvantage. His stature was short, his shoulders were not broad, his frame contracted or puny. He had a large head, a bigger head than even the giant Chau-wa-lanne, but his features were irregular; on one side of his face the profile was good, the other side defective. In most self-made men and women the left side, which controls the right hand, is most fully developed. That is the side we make ourself, the other is the side we are born with. On the left side there was divinity in Wili-wili-han's face, on the right clownishness, like the right side of Lincoln's face.

The young soothsayer had worked hard to perfect his art, his nearness to the infinite, it showed in the serious, though not harmonious lines of his countenance. In the camp adjoining to that of the widow and her gifted son dwelt Woakus or Grey Fox, the famous captain. Besides his squaw he had several sons and daughters, including one girl named Lena-kit-chita, or Indian Summer. How she got this strange sobriquet none can tell, but it came to be most appropriate as events shaped themselves. She of course knew young Wili-wili-han, and always spoke up for him when others ridiculed. "He will be the greatest one among you", was the tenor of her championship. When the other boys and girls threw stones at him and would not let him play their games, Lena-kit-chita would always run to his side, and comfort and amuse him. She was a stalwart, lioness of a girl, and once or twice soundly thrashed well-grown boys for molesting her favorite.

Wili-wili-han was shy by nature, he had limited powers of expressing himself, but as best as a "silent man" can he conveyed his gratitude to his fair protectress. She often stopped at his humble lodge and asked him to accompany her on walks in the woods. Neither would speak much on these excursions, but both were thinking deeply.

Once, and once only did Wili-wili-han kiss the smooth, round cheek of his friend, but one kiss to a spiritual man means more than a thousand to a lecher. The gist of the young man's thoughts were that some day, when he was famous, he would ask Lena-kit-chita to marry him. She must care for him else why would she stay away from her other and livelier companions to amuse him, why would she fight for him, why would she ask him to go with her on so many walks in the forest, why would she hold up her smooth, firm cheek so that he might kiss her. But again, why should she marry one so eccentric, so physically disproportionate, so ill born, so poor. But he was underrating himself, he had a distinctive personality, and was far from being what would be called homely; his mystic gifts had already found him marked favor with the king. He was now, a noble-man by courtesy; every honor accorded to rank was exhibited towards him. All he would have needed was a little courage, and Lena-kit-chita was his, in those days. While he was hesitating and repining, Chau-wa-lanne had espied the fair maid himself. He commanded that she be brought before him, and she was delighted at this signal honor.

Arraying herself in her best, in a coat of the breasts of male wild pigeons, with a collar and cuffs of opossum fur, she attended the regal youth at his lodge house on the summit of Mount Eagle.

It had been a case of love at first sight with Chau-wa-lanne when he had seen her at a distance; Lena-kit-chita sixteen year old girl that she was, had always admired her stalwart king. Now when they met face to face, each was illuminated with a consuming love. Much as she had secretly cared for Wili-wili-han, she had always felt that he lacked something now she knew, it was physical beauty. Before her stood the great slim muscular Chau-wa-lanne, six feet five inches in height, with the features of an eagle, the muscular development of a panther. He seemed typical of the world he ruled: above him soared the eagles, screaming their treble fury, nearby growled the pet panther. Back of him was ranged his personal body-guard, composed of youths of his own age, and almost similar height. Lena-kit-chita stood probably five feet eight; she towered above Wili-wili-han it seemed, but in the presence of her king she felt a more equable sense of proportion. She could hardly speak for her rapt admiration of his charms.

When he talked his attractiveness was enhanced. He had a clear, well-modulated voice, his manners would have captivated any woman, he was so considerate, so polished. It was a clear sense of noblesse oblige. There is no reason for a king to pursue a long courtship when he knows all about the object of his love. He had investigated Lena-kit-chita before he sent for her, her birth he was familiar with before; her character had been pronounced spotless. She was not surprised when he wound up the interview by asking her to become his bride. He would not have invited her to climb Mount Eagle for less. She accepted with such genuine cordiality that the young King felt assured that he had found a jewel, a loving mate. She was asked to set a date, naming a day two moons hence.

The wedding, which occurred in the beautiful month of May, was attended by Indians from far and wide. Chief among the participants was Wili-wili-han, who had lately assumed the post of High Priest, upon the death of the venerable redman, Pethak-wonn, or Thundergust, who had performed this office for so many years. If he was grieved to see his one and only love marrying another, he made no outward show of it. He had been one of the first to congratulate Lena-kit-chita when her betrothal was announced; it seemed to give him an unalloyed pleasure. There was no pettiness, no rancor in his nature; life was an open book to this philosopher.

After the ceremony the happy couple, who had eyes for no one but themselves, went for a short trip down the Creek, in a sumptuously decorated canoe built of white or "canoe" birch-bark. The royal bridegroom was his own steersman while the bride reclined on cushions and robes of mountain cat and otter. They were so overjoyed to be away together that they prolonged the trip considerably; six moons had passed before they returned to their eyrie. Soon after they came back, Lena-kit-chita was seized with a heavy cold, which developed into pneumonia. It seemed for a time as if she must die, and leave all her happiness. But Wili-wili-han, who had been summoned to minister to her, pulled her through the crisis, drawing her back from the yawning jaws of death. Though she escaped the grim reaper she did not improve as her watchful husband thought she should.

There was a racking cough, an emaciation, a listlessness that betokened perhaps a permanent affection of the lungs. She had chills and fever, which reduced her vitality lower each succeeding day.

To make matters worse the summer was waning fast and the long rains which would last until the advent of winter were an appalling prospect. When the equinoxial rains betokened that summer was no more, Lena-kit-chita moaned and cried for the fair days that had gone. "If I couldn't improve in sunshine, how could I do better in constant storm", she wailed as she tossed her shapely form about on her couch of buffalo robes. But she was really not a complainer; she had no desire to make Chau-wa-lanne's lot harder than it was. She was suffering intensely, and anyone would have bemoaned a fate which offered no respite. There was a natural drainage on Mount Eagle, there were no pools to hold water, but even at that, the constant drip, drip, drip was disheartening, depressing. One morning, when there had been a steady downpour for five days, the fair sufferer underwent a severer chill than usual; Wili-wili-han who had occupied a tepee near the royal quarters ever since she had been stricken, was hastily summoned. He applied all his remedies, and saved her heart's action from collapse. When she recovered sufficiently to be calm, she sent for Chau-wa-lanne.

"I am better, my beloved, but I have strong reason to believe that I will never get well." The king tried to encourage her, but she shook her curly head, "No, I can never improve while these storms continue; I wish that there was a season like my name,

Indian Summer, a season following the summer, when the glad sunshine of happier days would succeed the depressing equinoxial rains, a period of warmth and life, before we feel the winter's blast.

I have only rain and snow to look forward to now; the rains chill me, the mound of the snows will prepare the way for the mound which will soon be heaped above my remains." She could say no more after this; sobbing she sank back on her pillow exhausted. Both the King and Wili-wili-han were deeply moved by her words; they realized the truth of what she said, but they seemed powerless to alter climatic conditions. They stood in silence before the fair invalid, until a drooping of her eyelids told them that she had fallen into a doze. Then the two powerful men of tribe withdrew, each trembling with a sense of his own impotence against the forces of Nature. As they stepped outside, the drip from the eaves trickled upon them, and ran down their backs. Chau-wa-lanne turned, and laid his sinewy hand on the wise man's shoulder. "Soothsayer," he said, impressively, "I have a favor to ask of you." "Anything I can do will be my greatest pleasure, sire," Wili-wili-han replied.

"You have infinite power, or as nearly so as mortal can possess it," the king resumed, "won't you intercede with the forces of nature and restore the health of my beloved queen?" "I have tried in every way, master," answered the wise man, "but of no avail; my medical potations have sufficed to a certain point but no further, my fervent prayers may have kept her alive, but in a sad and almost hopeless state." "But can't you," broke in Chau-wa-lanne, "ask the Great Spirit, the Gitchie-Manitto whom we have always served, to send a new season, whose sunbeams will restore the color to Lena-kit-chita's cheeks, and make despondent nature glad again, before the pall of the ice king?" "I do not see how mortal would dare to expect such a benefice," replied the soothsayer, "Gitchie-Manitto created seasons which seemed best suited to the needs of the most of us. We might all be rebuked for our presumption."

"Wili-wili-han," said the King, "Lena-kit-chita is a young woman of saintly life; she should be spared to the redmen as an example of goodness; I firmly believe the Great Spirit will listen." "Whatever you say is true, my king," said the wise man, "your faith gives me the strength to ask this blessing. I will tonight retire to an inaccessible cliff on this same mountain, and ask as you request."

Chau-wa-lanne shook him warmly by the hand, and the two men parted.

The King re-entered the lodge-house, finding his queen awake. "Darling Lena-kit-chita," he whispered, "Wili-wili-han has promised to ask the Great Spirit to send a new season, an Indian Summer, beautiful like yourself, to bring you back to health, to make all Indians happy, before the onset of winter." The sufferer smiled cheerfully: "Wili-wili-han is a great soul," she faltered, "I know he is favored by the unseen power, I have perfect faith in his accomplishment if he petitions it." After fasting all day, at dusk, the High Priest attired himself in his official robes, hanging to his person every talisman and cabalistic token he possessed. At dark he emerged from his tent into the drizzling rain. The leaves on the trees were bedraggled and falling; the earth soggy and oozing; he could appreciate that it was a time when invalids would go downward instead of upward. He followed a trail to the crag known as the Eagle Rock which overhung Machtando, or as it is now called the Bald Eagle Valley. There he paused, with arms uplifted, and muttered his mystic invocation.

When the words were said, he fell on his face, and in a loud, but respectful voice chanted, "Oh, Great Spirit, who has ever been the friend of the race of Chau-wa-lanne, and have favored this young ruler ofttimes, think of the sufferings long continued of his queen. My prayers and libations have failed; there seems but one chance to restore her back to health; this one chance is the creation of a new season, a fresh spell of sunshine and color, to succeed the dreary pall of the rains. Oh, Great Spirit, ordain it for the glory of Lena-kit-chita, of Indian Summer, best and truest of her tribe. Let her live on as an example of purity and godliness to her race. One and all need this new season, it will bring joy and hope to the entire people of Lenni-Lenape."

It was then and there that he heard the rustle of an angel's wing. He arose, and walked slowly, and sadly back along the trail in the drizzling rain. Out of the darkness had come an answer of blessing to the in- valid, but it also contained evil tidings as to the future of his race. Furthermore he could not stifle the thought that Lena-kit-chita might have been his wife, his share of the glory of Indian Summer. He lay awake all that night, thinking over his message from the Infinite, of his lost love, and how he wished to prove his unselfishness.

Towards dawn the patter of raindrops ceased, and he heard birds singing in the trees. Could he be in a trance? A shaft of sunlight, like midsummer, shot through the flap of the tent. He got up, and looked out, a scene of rare beauty met his gaze. All the autumn foliage was gleaming in the warm sunlight, the mauve of the beeches, the buff of the hickories, the ochre of the tulip trees, the yellow gold of the maples, the maroon of the oaks, the titian red of the sumacs. The woodbine which curved cocoon-like over cedars and pines, was magenta colored in contrast to the dark greens of its captives. The grasses were pink and gold, the earth was dry and firm. Over all hung a delicate haze, like a mantle of the Great Spirit shutting out the rains, and leaving in only the light.

Overjoyed he ran to Lena-kit-chita's lodge; finding her standing at the door, a look of rapture in her face. "Oh, friend and queen," he cried out, "this is your weather, your days for good health and happiness, it is all for the glory of Indian Summer, of Queen Lena-kit-chita!" The Queen looked at him; her voice was choked with emotion. "How can I express my gratitude, wise High Priest; from an invalid, hopeless of ever getting well, you have made me a well woman supremely happy in this beautiful world." "You owe no thanks to me," said Wili-wili-han, "it is to the Great Spirit that we owe everything, who has done this for you, to show that he loved the Indian race. Our people will always be remembered while this, the fairest, most mystic season of the year exists." "Do you mean that some time our seed may grow less?" said the valiant King Chau-wa-lanne, who appeared on the scene at this minute. "Surely there will never be any just like your Queen and your Majesty," replied the wise man, evading the question. But in his heart he knew the awful tragedy which loomed ahead of his people, like a rock hidden by mist, in a ship's course; the voice in the night which granted his petition had told him this. He bowed, and walked away, feeling sick at heart, for he knew that his race would vanish, only to live as ghosts, filmy and vaporous as the mists of Indian Summer. With such a fate no wonder Gitchie-Manitto could give them a new season, an Indian Summer as a last indulgence.

The Indians' Twilight:
The Story of Grandfather Pine

According to Daniel Mark, born in 1835 (died 1922), when the aged Seneca Indian, Isaac Steel, stood beside the moss-grown stump of the giant "Grandfather Pine" in Sugar Valley, in the early Autumn of 1892, he was silent for a long while, then placing his hands over his eyes, uttered these words: "This is the Indians' Twilight; it explains many things; I had heard from Billy Dowdy, when he returned to the reservation in 1879, that the tree had been cut by Pardee, but as he had not seen the stump, and was apt to be credulous, I had hoped that the report was untrue; the worst has happened."

Then the venerable Redman turned away, and that same day left the secluded valley, never to return.

The story of the Grandfather Pine, of Sugar Valley, deserves more than the merely passing mention already accorded it in forestry statistics and the like. Apart from being probably the largest white or cork pine recorded in the annals of Pennsylvania sylviculture—breast high it had to be deeply notched on both sides, so that a seven foot cross-cut saw could be used on it—it was the sacred tree of the Seneca Indians, and doubtless of the earlier tribes inhabiting the country adjacent to the Allegheny Mountains and the West Branch Valley.

It was a familiar landmark for years, standing as it did near the mouth of Chadwick's Gap, and could be seen towering above its fellows, from every point in Sugar Valley, from Schracktown, Loganton, Eastville and Carroll.

Professor Ziegler tells us that the maximum or heavy growth of white pine was always on the winter side of the inland valleys; the biggest pines of Sugar Valley, Brush Valley and Penn's Valley were all along the southern ridges.

Luther Guiswhite, now a restauranteur in Harrisburg, moving like a voracious caterpillar easterly along the Winter side of Brush Valley, gradually destroyed grove after grove of superb original white pines, the Gramley pines, near the mouth of Gramley's Gap, which Professor Henry Meyer helped to "cruise", being the last to fall before his relentless juggernaut.

Ario Pardee's principal pineries were mostly across the southern ridge of Nittany Mountain, of Sugar Valley, on White Deer Creek, but the tract on which the Grandfather Pine stood ran like a tongue out of Chadwick's Gap into Sugar Valley, almost to the bank of Fishing Creek. It is a well known story that after the mammoth pine had been cut, Mike Courtney, the lumberman-philanthropist's woods boss, offered $100 to anyone who could transport it to White Deer Creek, to be floated to the big mill at Watsontown, where Pardee sawed 111,000,000 feet of the finest kind of white pine between 1868 and 1878.

The logs of this great tree proved too huge to handle, even after being split asunder by blasting powder, crushing down a number of trucks, and were left to rot where they lay. Measured when prone, the stem was 270 feet in length, and considering that the stump was cut breast high, the tree was probably close to 276 feet from root to tip. The stump is still visible and well worthy of a visit.

In addition to boasting of the biggest pine in the Commonwealth, one of the biggest red hemlocks also grew in Sugar Valley, in the centre of Kleckner's woods, until it was destroyed by bark peelers in 1898. It dwarfed the other original trees in the grove, mostly superb white hemlocks, and an idea of its size can be gained when it is stated that "breast high" it had a circumference of 30 feet.

When Billy Dowdy, an eccentric Seneca Indian, was in Sugar Valley he told Squire Mark the story of the Grandfather Pine, then recently felled, and while the Indian did not visit the "fallen monarch" on that occasion, he refrained from so doing because he said he could not bear the sight. The greatest disaster that had yet befallen the Indians had occurred, one that they might never recover from, and meant their final elimination as factors in American history.

Dowdy seemed unnerved when he heard the story of the demolition of the colossal pine, and it took several visits to the famous Achenbach distillery to steady his nerves so that he could relate its history to his old and tried friend the 'Squire. In the evening, by the fireside, showing emotion that rarely an Indian betrays, he dramatically recited the story of the fallen giant.

Long years ago, in the very earliest days of the world's history, the great earth spirit loved the evening star, but it was such an unusual and unnatural attachment, and so impossible of consummation that the despairing spirit wished to end the cycle of existence and pass into oblivion so as to forget his hopeless love. Accordingly, with a blast of lightning he opened his side and let his anguish flow away. The great gaping wound is what we of today call Penn's Cave, and the never ending stream of anguish is the wonderful shadowy Karoondinha, now renamed John Penn's Creek.

As time went on fresh hopes entered the subterranean breast of the great earth spirit, and new aspirations towards the evening star kindled in his heart of hearts. His thoughts and yearnings were constantly onward and upward towards the evening star. He sought to bridge the gulf of space and distance that separated him from the clear pure light of his inspiration. He yearned to be near, even if he could not possess the calm and cold constellation so much beyond him. He cried for an answer, but none came, and thought that it was distance that caused the coldness, and certainly such had caused the great disappointment in the past.

His heart was set on reaching the evening star, to have propinquity with the heavens. Out of his strong hopes and deep desires came a tall and noble tree, growing in eastern Sugar Valley, a king among its kindred, off there facing the shining, beaming star. This tree would be the symbol of earth's loftiest and highest aspirations, the bridge between the terrestrial and the celestial bodies. It was earth's manliest, noblest and cleanest aspiration, standing there erect and immobile, the heavy plates of the bark like gilt-bronze armor, the sparse foliage dark and like a warrior's crest.

The Indians, knowing full well the story of the hopeless romance of the earth spirit and the evening star, or Venus, as the white men called it, venerated the noble tree as the connecting link between two manifestations of sublimity. They only visited its proximity on sacred occasions because they knew that the grove over which it dominated was the abode of spirits, like all groves of trees of exceptional size and venerable age.

The cutting away of most of the bodies of original pines has circumscribed the abode of the spiritual agencies until they are now almost without a lodgement, and must go wailing about cold and homeless until the end of time, unless spiritual insight can touch our materialistic age and save the few remaining patches of virgin trees standing in the valley of the Karoondinha, the "Stream of the Never Ending Love", now known by the prosaic cognomen of "Penn's Valley".

The Tom Motz tract is no more, the Wilkenblech, the Bowers and the Meyer groves are all but annihilated. Where will the spirits rest when the last original white pine has been ripped into boards at The Forks, now called Coburn? No wonder that Artist Shearer exclaimed, "The world is aesthetically dead!"

The Indians were greatly dismayed at the incursion of white men into their mountain fastnesses, so contrary to prophecy and solemn treaties, and no power seemed to stem them as they swept like a plague from valley to valley, mountain to mountain. The combined military strategy and bravery of Lenni-Lenape, Seneca, Cayuga, Tuscarora and Shawnee failed before their all-conquering advance. How to turn back this white peril occupied the mind and heart of every Indian brave and soothsayer.

One evening just as Venus in the east was shedding her tranquil glory over the black outline of the pine covered ranges of the Nittanies, a mighty council of warriors and wise men, grave and reverent, assembled under the Grandfather Pine. Hitherto victory, while it had rested with the white invaders, had not been conclusive; there was still hope, and the Indians meant to battle to the end.

It was during this epochal conclave that a message was breathed out of the dark shaggy pigeon-haunted tops of the mighty tree. Interpreted it meant that the Indian braves and wise men were reminded that this great pine reached from heaven to earth, and by its means their ancestors used to climb up and down between the two regions. In a time of doubt and anxiety like this, the multitudes, conferring beneath the tree, were invited to ascend to hold a council with the stars, to exchange views and receive advice as to how the insidious white invader could be kept in proper bounds, and to preserve the glory and historic dignity of the Indian races. The stars, which were the spirits of undefeated warriors and hunters and huntresses of exceptional prowess— their light was the shimmer of their silvery targets—had always been the allies of the red men.

In solemn procession the pick of the assemblage of Indian warriors and wise men ascended the mighty tree, up, up, up, until their forms became as tiny specks, and disappeared in the dark lace-like branches which merged with the swart hues of the evening heavens. They set no time for their return, for they were going from the finite to the infinite, but they would be back to their beloved hills and valleys in plenty of time, and with added courage and skill, to end the regime of the pale faced foes.

Every wife and mother and sweetheart of a warrior who took this journey was overjoyed at the privilege accorded her loved one, and none begrudged being left behind to face the enemy under impaired leadership, or the risk of massacre, as in due course of time the elite would return from above and rescue them from their cruel tormentors.

Evidently out of space, out of time, was almost the equivalent of "out of sight, out of mind" for all who had witnessed the chosen band of warriors and warlocks ascend the pine, even the tiny babes, reached maturity and passed away, and yet they had not returned or sent a message. The year that the stars fell, in 1833, brought hopes to the anxious ones, but never a falling star was found to bring tidings from that bourne above the clouds.

Generation after generation came and went, and the ablest leaders still were absent counseling with the stars. Evidently there was much to learn, much to overcome, before they were fully fledged to return and battle successfully.

The succeeding generations of Indian braves fought the white foes as best they could, yet were ever being pushed back, and they were long since banished from Sugar Valley where grew the Grandfather Pine. Occasionally those gifted with historic lore and prophecy journeyed to the remote valley to view the pine, but there were no signs of a return of the absent chieftains.

It was a long and weary wait. Were they really forsaken, or were there affairs of great emergency in the realm of the evening star that made them tarry so long? They might be surprised on their return to find their hunting territories the farms of the white men, their descendants banished to arid reservations on La Belle Riviere and beyond. They had left in the twilight; they would find the Indians' Twilight everywhere over the face of the earth. It was a sad prospect, but they never gave up their secret hope that the visitors to strange lands would return, and lead a forlorn hope to victory.

Then came upon the scene the great lumberman, Ario Pardee. The bed of White Deer Creek was "brushed out" from Schreader Spring to Hightown, to float the millions of logs that would pile up wealth and fame for this modern Croesus. What was one tree, more or less—none were sacred, and instead of being the abode of spirits, each held the almighty dollar in its heart.

Pardee himself was a man of dreams and an idealist, vide Lafayette College, and the portrait of his refined and spiritual face by Eastman Johnson, in the rotunda of "Old Pardee". Yet it was too early a day to care for trees, or to select those to be cut, those to be spared; the biggest tree, or the tree where the buffaloes rubbed themselves, were alike before the axe and cross-cut; all must fall, and the piratical-looking Blackbeard Courtney was the agent to do it.

Perhaps trees take their revenge, like in the case of the Vicar's Oak in Surrey, as related by the diarest Evelyn—shortly after it was felled one of the choppers lost an eye and the other broke a leg. Mike Courtney, it is reported, ended his days, not in opulent ease lolling in a barouche in Fairmount Park with Hon. Levi Mackey, as had been his wont, but by driving an ox-team in the wilds of West Virginia!

The Grandfather Pine was brought to earth after two days of chopping by an experienced crew of woodsmen; when it fell they say the window lights rattled clear across the valley in Logansville (now Loganton). It lay there prone, abject, yet "terrible still in death", majestic as it sprawled in the bed that had been prepared for it, with an open swath of forest about that it had maimed and pulled down in its fall.

Crowds flocked from all over the adjacent valleys to see the fallen monarch, like Arabs viewing the lifeless carcass of a mighty lion whose roar had filled them with terror but a little while before.

Then came the misfortune that the tree was found to be commercially unprofitable to handle, and it was left for the mould and the moss and the shelf-fungi to devour, for little hemlocks to sprout upon.

Billy Dowdy was in the West Branch Valley trying to rediscover the Bald Eagle Silver Mine—old Uriah Fisher, of the Seventh Cavalry, can tell you all about it—when the story was told at "Uncle Dave" Cochran's hotel at Pine Station that Mike Courtney had conquered the Grandfather Pine. It is said that a glass of the best Reish whiskey fell from his nerveless fingers when he heard the news. He suddenly lost all interest in the silver mine on the Bald Eagle Mountain, which caused him to be roundly berated by his employers, and dropping everything, he made for Sugar Valley to verify the terrible story. 'Squire Mark assured him that it was only too true; he had strolled over to Chadwick's Gap the previous Sunday and saw the prostrate Titan with his own eyes.

The Indians' twilight had come, for now the picked band of warriors and warlocks must forever linger in the star-belt, unless the earth spirit, out of his great love, again heaved such a tree from his in-most creative consciousness.

Sometimes the Indians notice an untoward bright twinkling of the stars, the evening star in particular, and they fancy it to be reassuring messages from their marooned leaders not to give up the faith, that sometimes they can return rich in wisdom, fortified in courage, ready to drive the white men into the sea, and over it to the far Summer Islands. When the stars fell on the thirteenth of November, 1833, it was thought that the starry hosts were coming down en masse to fight their battles, but not a single stellar ally ever reported for duty.

Old John Engle, mighty Nimrod of Brungard's Church (Sugar Valley), on the nights of the Northern Lights, or as the Indians called them, "The Dancing Ghosts", used to hear a strange, weird, unaccountable ringing echo, like exultant shouting, over in the region of the horizon, beyond the northernmost Allegheny ridges. He would climb the "summer" mountain all alone, and sit on the highest summits, thinking that the wolves had come back, for he wanted to hear them plainer. In the Winter of 1859 the distant acclamation continued for four successive nights, and the Aurora covered the entire vault of heaven with a preternatural brilliance. Great bars of intensely bright light shot out from the northern horizon and broke in mid-sky, and filled the southern skies with their incandescence. The sky was so intensely red that it flared as one great sheet of fire, and engulfed the night with an awful and dismal red light. Reflected on the snow, it gave the earth the appearance of being clothed in scarlet.

The superstitious Indians, huddled, cold and half-clad, and half-starved in the desert reservations, when they saw the fearful glow over beyond Lake Erie, and heard the distant cadences, declared that they were the signal fires and the cries for vengeance of the Indian braves imprisoned up there in star-land, calling defiance to the white hosts, and inspiration to their own depleted legions, the echo of the day of reckoning, when the red men would come to their own again, and finding their lost people, lead them to a new light, out of the Indians' twilight.

VI.
Why We Keep Returning
to Happy Valley

One of the most striking and oft-remarked phenomena of the Nittany Valley—and indeed of all the region of central Pennsylvania—is the fact that almost everyone who lives here for any length of time seems to have an irresistible desire to return as often as possible.

This is most obvious in the alumni of Penn State, all 700,000 of them (560,00 still living), who as students may have spent only a few years at Penn State, but who yearn to return year after year, not only for football games, but for the Central Pennsylvania Festival of the Arts and numerous other activities throughout the year. The region has also become one of the top retirement locations, as older alumni feel a strong desire return to spend their declining years in the area.

But all this is equally true of students and alumni, and also of large numbers of faculty, as well as local residents unconnected to the University who move away for jobs or other reasons but keep coming back for visits, events, retirement—or who keep looking for new jobs in the area that will allow them to move back.

Is there something in the water, or in the breezes that come down from the surrounding mountains that keep us coming back— or at least longing to come back? There seems to be an attractive power in the mountains and valleys of this region that calls us.

Of course, sociologists have a lot of dry data and theories, economic, social, or psychological, to explain all this. But none of them seem to match up with the feelings that really make us want to come back.

The following legend of King Wi-Daagh's spell, however, no matter how mystical or supernatural it seems to skeptics, seems to offer a more telling and satisfying explanation.

King Wi-Daagh was an important historical personage in Pennsylvania history. At the time of the grant to William Penn of the colony of Penn's Woods in 1681, Wi-Daagh was the powerful chief—often referred to as king—of all the Susquehannocks inhabiting roughly the area west of the main course of the Susquehanna River, between the West Branch of the Susquehanna River to the north, and the course of the Juniata River to the south.

On September 13, 1700, Wi-Daagh entered into a treaty allowing the Penn Family to explore the region of his "kingdom." This furnished the occasion for John Penn, son of William Penn, to commence his historic journey—of which Shoemaker records many legends and stories—up the famed Karoondinha ("Stream of Neverending Love" referred to in several legends in this collection), as a result of which that stream was renamed John Penn's Creek in his honor. Of course, the settlers did not only explore, but immediately interpreted the treaty as permission to move into the area.

The camp and burial site along Antes Creek of King Wi-Daagh (known as Lochabar, meaning "Lake Where the Deer Shed Horns") still exists. It is marked by a 41-foot high column, which was salvaged from the capital building in Harrisburg after a fire, and shipped to commemorate King Wi-Daagh by Col. Sanderson, the great grandson of the famous Indian scout, Covenhoven. The inscription on the column reads:

King Wi-Daagh
King of the Susquehannocks
Whose wigwam was here
Executed treaty with Wm. Penn
September 13, 1700
Conveying Susquehanna River
and Lands Adjoining in Consideration of
"A Parcel of English Goods"
Erected September 13, 1900

The legend recounts King Wi-Daagh's regret and feelings of being taken advantage of in the transaction, which historians confirm. But the real gist of the legend and story is the spell Wi-Daagh worked on visitors to the region—or those simply passing through—

whom he would go out on the paths to meet and present with a shell. Once the shell was proffered, the spell took hold, and the hapless recipient found himself or herself subject to an irresistible desire to return to Wi-Daagh's camp within a year. According to legend, Wi-Daagh not only worked this spell while he was alive, but his wraith or ghost continued to work it long after his death.

The next time you, or anyone who has once been in the Nittany Valley, suddenly feels a strong urge to go back to Penn State or to any of the areas that were once part of Wi-Daagh's kingdom, just smile and remember this legend, and you will immediately understand why the feeling seems so irresistible.

King Wi-Daagh's Spell

It was the unvarying custom, and perhaps the chief peculiarity of King Wi-daagh, the last ruler of the Susquehannah Indians, that any of his subjects who happened to lay eyes on him, must return and see him again one year from the date. This he imagined instilled a proper respect for his exalted station, especially when the person who had looked at him would have to travel two hundred miles through forests drifted with snow to repeat the performance. If he but knew it, his subjects came to hate the sight of him for this very reason. But he had other faults. As a financier he was a failure, even for an Indian. His bargain with the Proprietary Government in September, 1700, a century after his great ancestor Pipsisseway's military triumphs, when he deeded the fertile Otzinachson Valley to the Penn family for a few trinkets and a bale of English goods, will stand out as the most one-sided land deal in history.

King Wi-daagh was very susceptible to flattery, a few grandiose compliments delivered to him by persons of the proper rank and he would give away anything. These were probably used by Penn's emissaries and if they had carried the farce much further he might have given them his birthright and handed back the trinkets and the bundle of goods. Though he ever regretted the sale, he kept it mostly to himself, which is to his credit. But to the day of his death he was pompous and overbearing to his kind, exaggerating trifles and glossing over the really important events in life. As long as his followers came back the following year after having seen him, he was satisfied. To put people to trouble seemed to be his chief delight. He was letting some splendid energy go to waste.

Wi-daagh's favorite walk was from his palace, which consisted of a many roomed cavern near the source of Antes Creek, along the stream, and thence westward to a small spring, where in his youth he had met clandestinely an Indian maid of inferior birth. Along the creek was the favorite pathway for Indians traveling north or south, and he invariably met troops of victims on every stroll. Much as they originally revered this august symbol of royalty, they hated the idea of having to come back a year from the date of their chance meetings with him.

To each Indian who met him he handed a piece of shell, curiously carved, and when a year later the bearer returned, it was broken in half by the Kings chamberlain, as a sort of receipt to prove that the Indian had fulfilled his obligation. As a result of this oppressive custom, the meadows in the vicinity of Wi-daaghs abode, afterwards the scene of his unequal bargain with the Quakers, were always thronged with Indians.

Oftentimes he would keep them waiting for days before collecting their bits of wampum, which he did personally. He claimed he had a great memory for faces, and would sometimes accuse a redman of being a substitute sent by the person who had actually seen him the year before. He would talk loud and threaten, but unless his mood changed before sunset, as it usually did, it meant death to the alleged substitute. The Indians, to avoid these unpleasant complications, would have avoided the trail along the creek, that their monarch frequented, had it not been that forseeing this very thing, he forbid his subjects to pass north or south any other way. Some did go many miles out of their course to keep clear of him, but spies reported them, and in some cases they fell into the hands of hostile tribes, whose penalties were more severe than Wi-daagh's. The only comfortable way to avoid their king was to stay at home, and Indians who had to travel east and west were envied, but some of these who were unlucky enough to have crossed the Susquehanna, and met the King at the spring, were forced to return like the hapless travelers on the trailway of Antes Creek.

As he grew older he was mortified by the knowledge that most of his subjects acknowledged the Penn family, and not himself as the real rulers of the realm. He protested that he merely thought he was selling the Englishmen right of way through the Susquehanna Valley, he did not expect them to attempt to be his overlords. That was his feeble defense to go down through the ages against the paltry sum given him for his property. He was humiliated when one year his chamberlain reported to him that four hundred Indians whom he had met on his walks had failed to return to pay their respects at the expiration of the year. The official gave the King a certain number of shells each day he went walking, and in that way kept track of the size of the returning parties. A party of fifty innocent Juniata Indians who were found camping along the mountains at the south side of Nippenose Valley were seized and accused of being some of the renegades. Despite their protests that they had never been in that part of the country, all were sentenced to be burned at the stake. Had it not been that a delegation from the Proprietary Government happened along opportunely, this cruel sentence would have been carried out. One of the Quakers seeing the captives lying about in the hot sun in the meadow, bound hand and foot, learned their story from an interpreter and intimated to King Wi-daagh to abrogate the punishment. That night, while the Quakers slept, an ear was cut from each of the fifty prisoners, their goods confiscated, and they were turned loose. Even this sentence seemed shocking to the Quakers but it was too late for further protests. But the backbone of Wi-daagh's rule was crushed, he lived the balance of his life a broken-hearted man. Even before his death, his sons and sons-in-law were quarrelling over the remnants of his domain like buzzards struggling over a dying horse. Perhaps if he had not estranged his subjects by his silly idea of making those who saw him return in a year, he might have rallied them around him and forcibly broken his contract with the Penns. Only a handful of Indians, and mostly from his immediate household attended his funeral exercises. No doubt the bulk of his subjects feared they might be exacted to come back the next year and call on his corpse. Attired in full warriors regalia and with face painted, he was buried where the Fish-house now stands on the Lochabar estate. How the later owners of this magnificent property came to erect this little pagoda above the remains of the fallen chieftain, is unknowable and belongs properly to the subject of divination. If only the weight of the Fish-house could have weighed down the ghost, then the best interests of divine justice would have been conserved.

King Wi-daagh's ghost was as unhappy as the living tenement had been. He had not been in his grave a week before he acquired the habit of taking midnight strolls through the Gap to the small spring at the foot of the upper mountain. Few Indians travelled at night, as lights were uncertain and expensive, so there was little to relieve his churlish loneliness. But he was occasionally seen by redman from distant points, who were unlucky enough to build their campfires along the path. When he loomed up before them, from back of the blaze, he would hold out his hand as if trying to give something to the campers. Obviously a spirit could not do this, unless it be the double of a living person, and he would sink back into the gloom and vanish. For some odd reason, those who saw him always found themselves back in Antes Gap a year later, no matter if they had left there after their first visit vowing never to return.

They always met the regal ghost on their second visit, and he would flit about them like a hazy rainbow before he dwindled out of sight. After the second visit the travelers did not find it necessary to return.

When the Indians were driven out of their beloved valleys of Central Pennsylvania, they took especial care not to warn their white supplanters of King Wi-daaghs ghost and his propensity to make those who saw him pay a return visit. They would have a laugh on their haughty conquerors if a ghost with far less substance than a jelly-fish compelled them to do homage in this manner. It would be the triumph of Indian spirit over Anglo-Saxon matter. Many a self-important Scotch-Irishman, through a chance meeting with the spook, was compelled to tramp back from the Chillasquaque, the Mahantango, the Codorus or the Swatara. Why they came, they could not understand. As the anniversary approached they felt queer in the head, as they phrased it, and an unaccountable impulse started them in the direction of Antes Gap. They always felt easier after their second meeting with the ghost, but the trips usually wound up by a long siege of insobriety, and plenty of curses heaped on the offending apparition.

In a later day, after a hotel had been built at the northerly entrance to the Gap, travelers and farmers would come into the cozy barroom nights with hair standing on end, and eyes bloodshot and dilated, order a drink of whisky, look about to judge the crowd, and say, I saw an Indian, all gotten up in war paint in the Gap; I was scared out of a years growth when he tried to hand me something. At first the landlord attributed these Indian stories to the alcoholic properties of Nippenose Valley cider, or Rauchtown applejack, but as each frightened guest told a similar story, he concluded there must be something back of it. He also noticed that about a year after the first fright, the same men would turn up in the bar-room, considerably cooled down, but saying that they had just come from a second experience with the Indian, and this time they were sure it was a ghost. It helped the trade in the bar, and as time went on, the genial landlord saw through it all, and rumor had it he too had met King Wi-daagh. But the wives of the solid citizens who met him never became convinced. When they heard the story they laid it to too much good cheer at

Jersey Shore, or at the cozy hostelry in the gap. The ghost never appeared when two persons were together, or to folk in carriages or wagons. He reserved himself for lone pedestrians. Wi-daagh in life had a similar predilection. If he came upon one of his subjects alone, the wretched savage, awed by the presence of supreme highness often prostrated himself on his face. When a crowd were present, more reserve was displayed.

VII.
The Story of Warrior's Mark

Every book of legends needs a tragic love story. In stories of love, romance, and conquest it is rarely the climactic moments that determine (rather than merely reveal) the fate of two lovers. Rather, fates are forged like water shapes stone—slowly, almost imperceptibly

over time. In the minor moments, like the slow trickle of the water, a drama can develop.

This legend tells the story behind the name of the town of Warriors Mark, located just south of State College. Through the lies of a deceitful, malicious man, a maiden is led to believe that the man she loves, who is a Brave of an enemy tribe, has married another woman. When her lover comes to visit her, believing him to be untrue, she turns him in as a spy, and too late learns the truth.

Warrior's Mark: A Love Story

Like Warrior's Ridge, the name "Warrior's Mark" has had many meanings ascribed to it. Geographically speaking, it is a flat piece of table land, well drained and fruitful, an ideal gathering place for savages in the olden days. The historian, Jones, states that the name originated from the fact of certain oak trees in the vicinity having crescents or half moons cut upon them with hatchets, so deep that traces remained until recent years. The significance of them was known to the Indians alone; but it is evident that they were of importance, for, during the Revolutionary War, every time a band of Indians came into the valley, one or more fresh "warrior marks" were put upon the trees. The Indian path leading from Kittanning, through the valley of the Karoondinha, to the Susquehanna ran across this table land, and up to the breaking out of the Revolution a good-sized Indian village occupied the site.

Captain Logan, that noted redman for whom Logan Run in Huntingdon County and Logan Valley in Blair County are named, and one of the last Indians to leave the Juniata Valley, when asked concerning the true meaning of the "warrior marks" evaded the general question, but stated that he knew of some marks made by an Indian lover at the time of the great war between the Susquehannocks and Lenni Lenape about 1635, which led to serious troubles, at least for that particular redskin.

It appeared that for several years before the unsuccessful invasion of the Spruce Creek Valley by the Lenni Lenape, a well-defined system of scouting and spying was carried on by the Indians living north of the Tussey Mountains. The invasion was looked for during several years before it actually took place, consequently the Susquehannocks were enabled to understand the exact strength of their foes and crush them at the Battle of the Indian Steps near the famous Rock Springs not far from the present village of Baileyville, in Centre County. This battle, the greatest in the history of the Indians of Pennsylvania, left the various tribes in the position they were found by William Penn.

Captain Logan could describe the battle to the smallest detail, and it is a pity that he did not fall in with some historian during his lifetime, who could have transferred it to manuscript form. As it is, after passing orally through several generations, it has lost much of its directness and historical accuracy. But it is perpetuated in stirring verse by Central Pennsylvania's bard, John H. Chatham.

Among the spies employed by the Northern Indians was a certain young brave named Keneshaw. He came from that picturesque region now known as Brush Valley, not far from Penn's

Cave. He was a handsome, vigorous fellow, keen and alert, and his reports on the status of the presumed foemen was much prized even by the mighty war-lord of the Susquehannocks, Pipsisseway. He was said to be so cunning that no one in the hostile territory was aware of his repeated visits, which was considered remarkable, even in a forested country.

But he had his vulnerable point, for he was only human, and like most men it was his heart that led him to indiscretion. For one morning in crossing the table land of the warrior's marks he saw a beautiful Indian maiden. It was a bright day in February, the month of flying clouds, and he was homeward bound after securing some particularly valuable information as to the fighting strength of the Lenni Lenape. The air was invigorating, yet in the windwalls where the sun shone down there was a comforting warmth to the atmosphere. Keneshaw was feeling keenly alive and happy, the ideal mood in which to be when overtaken by the god of love. His alert senses told him that some one was coming toward him on the path, so he adroitly stepped behind a giant beech to wait until the danger passed. To his surprise it was not a proud young brave, or a suspicious old chief, but a very beautiful young maid.

Overcome by an impulse he could not resist, the hardened spy and wily diplomat stepped out from behind the tree and confronted the girl in the path. He had a winning smile, and he knew the Indian world and its ways, for it was a world strangely like ours, and the result produced was the same.

Alletah, the Lenni Lenape maid, smiled in return and felt no fear. The handsome couple became speedily well acquainted, so much so that the scout was not afraid to tell the girl all about himself. Between lovers there is always self-revelation, even when the confession is perilous.

But Alletah, her affections struck into flame by the suddenness of the meeting, was to be trusted, besides she had no personal grudge against the redmen of the north. But she frankly admitted the danger of ever being seen with this strange youth. It would mean death at the stake for her and an even more terrible end for Keneshaw if he was caught. And as their great love had been born under the spreading branches of the giant beech, its dry leaves palpitating in the February breeze, they would meet there, and there alone. It was a secluded spot, and could be approached by night, and gradually their plans for the future could be worked out under it.

The plan would be that when Keneshaw came into that region on his next spying trip he would carve a half moon very close to the roots of the tree, and Alletah when she found it would steal from her parents' lodge house at midnight and meet her lover at the sacred spot. She would manage to pass the tree every day, but if she should happen to miss it by bad weather or absence with her parents on hunting or fishing trips, Keneshaw would await her at the tree for several consecutive nights, until she appeared. Then, when they parted, they would carve away the half moon, so there could be no errors until the next time. The horned moon or Astarte was an Indian symbol of love or passion, therefore the most appropriate of warrior's marks!

When they parted Keneshaw threw his great arms about the beautiful Alletah and held her face so that he could look down into it, and carry away a lasting image, a likeness burned into his heart of hearts. And Alletah was a very beautiful maiden. She was not very tall, but was of plump and shapely build, and with, oh, such an exquisite face. By far the best feature of all was the eyes, the color of fairy stones, a peculiar changeable hue. By the campfire's ruddy glow they shone blue, but by daylight, under the flying clouds of February, they were brown, with lights of red and agate. By night her hair was golden, yet by day it seemed black, as befitting one of her race. But the waxy pallor of her face, the parchment pink of her thin lips was always the same. Her nose long and straight showed her descent from a line of warriors who were not afraid of death.

After many embraces, coupled with vows and protestations, Keneshaw turned from his new-found love and hurried on his way. He longed to look back, but it meant disaster to every Indian who refused to accept "good-bye"—God be with you until we meet again—as final. But the impression made was a deep one, especially as Keneshaw had never been in love before. Much as he adored his work as scout, he loved the fair Alletah more. And he managed to revisit the valleys about Warrior's Run more frequently than other parts of the territory of the Southern Indians, so that he could be near to where she resided. But the meeting of the lovers was always at the same place, under the giant beech on the table land. From February until September the romance continued unabated every moon. The last time that the pair were together they were particularly happy in each other's company. A definite hope for a speedy union was at hand.

The Lenni Lenape had decided to cross the Indian Steps and invade the country of the Susquehannocks, and in the confusion of a bloody war, Alletah would slip across the mountains and become the wife of her warrior lover. Then he would establish her in some secluded valley in the north until peace was restored and her family would forget that she ever lived. As this might sound heartless to modern readers, it would be well to state that there were no reconciliations among the Lenni Lenape, a daughter who married a foe was dead to them for all time.

It was a beautiful cloudless afternoon when the lovers parted. There was already a lavender tint to the leaves of the ancient beech. Among the dry grass a few belated stalks of boneset, iron-weed and Joe Pye weed bloomed triumphantly. The tops of the golden rods were grey, faded blonde beauties. The blue birds twittered as they flew about in companies, preparing for their migration. As Nature is loveliest at time of change, so it is said, seems a woman more beautiful at parting. Keneshaw was loath to go, and he clasped and unclasped his arms about the fair Alletah, as if filled with some presentiment that it would be for the last time. Why is it that cruel fate is made easier for us by such portends, and happier are those who are sensible enough to heed them? Yet his last words to Alletah were that he would be back the next moon. He did not look back as he hurried away.

When he reached the headquarters of his king on the banks of the West Branch of the Susquehanna, at the royal village of Tschimingy, he was made acquainted with a strange looking being, a pale-faced man, a native of France called Stephen Brule, who had in 1615 been the first white man to visit Pennsylvania. At that time he had come to induce the Susquehannocks to join the Hurons of Canada in making war on the Five Nations, which then occupied the "lake region" in central New York State. On this later occasion he had come on a friendly visit, but the mighty Pipsisseway had arranged that his favorite scout Keneshaw, upon his return from the South, should act as his escort through Northern Pennsylvania and New York, and see him safely into friendly territory in Canada. For no Indian living knew the forest paths like Keneshaw, and he was only a young man, so it must be inferred that the secrets of the forests were his special talent, his born aptitude.

It would be a long journey, however, and his smile left his lips, when the orders were given to him. Many moons must pass before he would again cross the Tussey Mountains to his love. But he loved his king, and it was a signal honor to be selected as guide to the white-faced stranger. Stephen Brule was popular with the Susquehannocks. He was a man of genial nature and prepossessing appearance. He is described as being of medium height, with reddish brown hair, a full beard, large blue eyes, and an aquiline nose; he was the true type of the adventurer or argonaut.

The next morning saw Keneshaw and Brule embarking on the West Branch in a canoe to begin their journey to the north by way of the North Fork of Sinnemahoning. A large assemblage was on the shores to wave "good-bye." Pipsisseway himself helped to launch the canoe in the sparkling waters. There were many who envied Keneshaw, and he wished they could read his heart and be satisfied with their lot.

As soon as the boat was out of sight up the river the king decreed the appointment of a new scout to temporarily visit the southern valleys. Some of the old warriors advised a young brave named Ko-She-Se-Glo, and he was accordingly selected for the post. Two months elapsed before he reached the vicinity of the giant beech tree. All this time Alletah had been on the alert watching for her lover's return, consequently she was quick to intercept the stranger wearing the headgear of the Susquehannocks, whom she noticed one morning leaning against the old tree.

Ko-She-Se-Glo was not handsome. He was the possessor of evil thoughts, which, according to the Indians, accounted for his ugliness. But he admired the opposite sex with all the ardor of an Adonis. Alletah approached him boldly, and asked him if he was acquainted with Keneshaw, a member of the same tribe. The new scout looked at the fair girl closely with his beady little black eyes, and thought that he understood the situation. Fie divined that the girl loved his predecessor, and would not favor any other Indian unless she felt that her lover had abandoned her. To have a love affair sub rosa with such a beautiful girl while attending to his official duties in the neighborhood was worth a lie at least. So when she asked him again about Keneshaw, he burst out into a coarse laugh.

"Keneshaw," he bellowed, "you know Keneshaw? Why he must have had a girl in every valley. But now he's married to a lovely wife, and will never come into these parts again."

Alletah's pale face flushed, and she bit her parchment-like lips to redness. It was hard to believe that she had been deceived, made a cat's-paw of, but it must be true since her lover had ceased coming. She questioned the stranger further on the subject. Keneshaw had been married some months, he said, but the bride had only lately heard of his love affairs when he was on his various trips and had induced him to take a post nearer home.

Deceived, deserted, loved by a married man, these were terrible things for Alletah to hear. Her savage blood turned her love to hate. She resolved then and there to have revenge somehow, yet she did not encourage the stranger, as she knew him to be an

Indian with evil thoughts. She parted from the visitor civilly, thanking him for his information, but after that she managed never to meet him again. All through the long winter she pined in her parents' lodge house. She could not eat, her sleep was broken by frightful dreams, she became as thin as a copperhead, as irritable as a lynx.

One day in April when the sun was shining with rare warmth through the bare trees she went for a stroll on the tableland. She felt so ill that she was seriously considering throwing herself over a precipice and ending it all; her walk would lead her in the direction of the gorge of Warrior's Run. As she passed the aged beech tree, which had been the scene of so many happy hours, she instinctively glanced at the huge smooth roots. To her amazement she saw a freshly cut half moon on one of them. Her heart began to beat against her breast so fast that she feared that the thumping would throw her to the ground. Her face flushed, her head became dizzy. She would meet Keneshaw that night as if nothing had happened, but alas that fair mood was fleeting. In another instant pride mastered her soul; revenge must be hers.

Turning on her heel, she quickly made for her father's lodge house. Going up to the old warrior, who was sitting on a red bear's hide, smoking and nodding in the sun, she fell on her knees, and tearfully announced that she had a confession to make. Her health had been poor because her conscience troubled her for her misdeeds. She had met and loved a spy from the Susquehannocks, had given him much information concerning her people. She repented of this wickedness, she gave herself up to die at the stake. At midnight coming the scout could be caught at a certain giant beech tree on the table land.

The old father, loving his tribe first, his family relations afterward, shed no tears on hearing this awful recital of perfidy. When she finished he reached for a war club which lay nearby and smote her over the forehead, knocking her senseless. There he left her while he strode along the village street to the abode of his chief. He quickly told him of the awful news.

The chief was, of course, indignant. He sent his bodyguard to bring Alletah to his presence. When she recovered consciousness she admitted the truth, and then she was ordered bound and gagged and the guards threw her like a sack of meal into an abandoned cabin. At midnight Keneshaw was surrounded at the trysting place, overpowered, gagged and carried into the presence of the chief who decreed that the spy and his traitor sweetheart should die together at the stake at daybreak. A huge pyre was built in the open space in front of the chieftain's castle. In the center of it a hard oak pole or stake was imbedded in the earth.

Just as the first red glare of the new day appeared above the Warrior's Ridge, the two renegade lovers were strapped back to back to the stake. Before the torch was applied by the chief the gags were removed, and he demanded of the victims if they had anything to say. Alletah, paler and more beautiful than ever, was the first to speak.

With a clear and composed voice she said, "My king, I do not claim any honor for my repentance and confession. I did it because I learned that my fellow-sufferer, who was once my lover, is married and had been deceiving me. Revenge prompted me to confess. I die a disgrace to my family and my tribe."

A great silence fell over the crowd at these words, which became more intense when Keneshaw began to speak.

"Great king," he said, "I am guilty of spying and have no excuses to make, but I swear I am not married. It is a false accusation. I die full of love for the fair girl who, tied to my back, will share my fate."

At these words, Alletah uttered a piercing scream, and her head fell down on her breast. She had swooned away.

But the details of the lovers' private lives mattered nothing to the angry multitude. As spies and traitors they must die, and they demanded that the torch be applied forthwith. The king first cut out Keneshaw's tongue with his scalping knife, and then applied the torch to the fagots. The cruel flames leaped up about the helpless victims. Keneshaw met his death in full consciousness, but Alletah never recovered her senses, therefore her end must have been a painless one. But both had given up their lives through a misunderstanding, through another's foul envy and jealousy. The searching flames soon swept everything bare, and then the crowd dispersed, feeling that they had witnessed the extinction of two human fiends.

Out in the Tussey Mountains, near the crystal spring, where Globe Run heads, where the old folks say the Indians used to camp, is a circular spot of ground where no grass or trees will grow. Barren in a plenteous land, it strikes terror to even an unfeeling heart. And that desert spot, the old folks say, is where Keneshaw and Alletah were burned at the stake nearly three hundred years ago. Perhaps fate leaves that spot desolate as a warning to other lovers, perhaps so that their memories may linger yet a while, a sort of Indian Abelard and Heloise. But as to the details the reader will have to supply himself, for the only person who could furnish the missing links was Captain Logan, who now sleeps at the mouth of Chickaclamoose.

VIII.
The Story of the Standing Stone
of Huntingdon

In the center of the town of Huntingdon stands an unusual
memorial: a thin stone column fourteen feet high and only six inches
square in width and depth. Strangely, the memorial commemorates

neither a person nor an event, but rather another stone memorial that stood there two stone memorials before this one.

On it is inscribed: "Onojutta Juniata Achsinnik Standing Stone erected Sept. 8th 1896 As a memorial of the ancient standing stone removed by the Indians in 1754." On another nearby plaque there is an announcement of the rededication on March 29, 1996.

Why does the town of Huntingdon dedicate a special memorial to an Indian stone marker that was removed by the Indians more than 250 years ago? Well, no one quite knows.

One legend states that at one time the Tuscaroras stole the original Standing Stone, but the other legends say Lenni Lenape got it back. Still others say that the original Standing Stone was built by other tribes of Indians before the Lenni Lenape even moved into the area. In any event, it seems that when the Lenni Lenape left the area, so did the original stone. No one knows how or where.

Nor does anyone know what was on the stone. Early settlers who claim to have seen it said that it was covered in characters, but no record remains of what they meant.

All that is known with any degree of credibility is that the Indians who were there when the first settlers arrived treated the original Standing Stone as a Very Sacred Monument—though some thought that it may have been merely a directional sign for the various paths that converged there.

In any and all events, there is a monument in the form of a fourteen-foot-high Standing Stone in Huntingdon, commemorating a Very Sacred mysterious Standing Stone of uncertain date and covered in characters no one knew the meaning of.

Here to whet your appetite for this mystery is one of the legends about that mysterious Standing Stone and its mysterious disappearance in 1754.

The Standing Stone:
A Legend of the Ancient Oneidas

All the historical traditions of the Oneidas laid stress on their southern origin. Certainly they had come from as far South as the valley of the Juniata, if not further. They were probably one of the many southern tribes which held possession of the Juniata country for a time. Where they originally came from is shrouded in mystery, if we exclude the premise that the Juniata Valley had been their permanent, old-time home. It is the antiquity of environment that appeals to every thinking man or woman. Those who travel to European countries think it is the "change of scene," but it is not, it is the desire to associate oneself with places where man has dwelt and struggled for centuries. As proof, give the average traveler a chance to decide between a trip to Spain or California. Unless he is a native Californian, and knows its history and people, he will choose Spain—every time.

When all know the antiquity of the Pennsylvania mountains better they will feel a deeper love for their home environment, and not seek to link themselves with some established proof of man's presence elsewhere.

It is not the visual beauty of the mountain or the ruined castle that we love, but the spiritual conception which is the history of the traditions of the human beings who peopled them. And more valuable than the stacks and stone crushers as upbuilders of character will be the ancient lore of the Juniata, if it be collected and tabulated before it is too late.

As far as can be learned there were three distinct Standing Stones concerned in the history of the Oneidas and their followers. The first one, the gift of the Gitchie-Manitto, was as old as man himself. The second one, described by John Harris, the younger, as he saw it in 1754, was fourteen feet high and six feet square, and stood on the right bank of Stone Creek near its mouth.

Soon after Harris saw it the Tuscarora Indians, who were related to the Oneidas, and came to the Standing Stone about 1712, removed the stone with them to Canada. The third stone, a part of which, rescued from the wall of a bake oven, is now in the library of Juniata College at Standing Stone Town or Huntingdon, was erected probably as a surveyor's corner on the same spot where the earlier stones had stood.

On the third stone was carved the names of many white men, surveyors, prospectors, politicians, with dates varying from 1768 to 1770. Before it was broken up to build a bake oven it was moved to near where the old court house in Huntingdon formerly stood. Much has been written concerning the two later stones, various have been the hypotheses advanced to account for them. Certain it is that the first two stones were used by the Indians to inscribe their glorious history, the records of their battles and triumphs.

The second stone had an antiquity not to be sneered at, having braved the elements for at least a century or from the time when the true Oneidas departed for the North.

The Tuscaroras attempted to imitate their glories, their veneration of a Standing Stone, their battles to defend it, but they were only pale shadows of the ancient people. The Indian burying ground, on the high land near where the old Presbyterian Church stood, at Huntingdon, was very extensive when found by the first settlers. But it gave no idea of the vast number of interments in it, or of its venerable age. It is stated by those who heard it from the aged Indian story tellers that the main body of the Oneidas departed for what is now New York State about the beginning of the seventeenth century, few lingered on until after the Tuscaroras arrived.

Jones in his "History of the Juniata Valley" quotes Dr. B.S. Barton, an authority, as stating that Oneida meant "Standing Stone." A similar definition is given in the "Handbook of American Indians," published by the United States Government. With so much diversity of opinion as usually exists regarding Indian words, it is probably correct.

When the Oneidas were in their glory at Standing Stone, theirs was an Indian metropolis. It is stated that between three and four thousand redmen resided in and about the giant settlement. The buildings were of a permanent type of construction, with streets and alleys terminating in a basilica or public meeting place, in the center of which stood the sacred Standing Stone. There on New Year's Day, with great display and ceremony the high priests performed the rite of chiseling the tribe's achievements for the past twelve-month on the stone. Sacrifices were offered up, there was fasting, prayer, dancing and song, to commemorate the valorous deeds of the Oneidas.

The tradition was that the Great Spirit gave the stone to his favorite people with the understanding that they perform some great deed each year, worthy of recording. It was to be carved on the stone annually on the anniversary of its gift from the Gitchie-

Manitto. The appearance of some of the buildings in Standing Stone Town of the Oneidas is worthy of description. The great settlement was surrounded by two rows of palisades eighteen feet high; in the ramparts were two gates, one facing the west, over which were erected three images of men carved out of wood, and draped with the scalps of their enemies. On the east side was another gateway similarly adorned. The western gate was three feet wide, the eastern gate two feet. Within the central palisade were several hundred lodge houses of imposing dimensions. These houses were built of logs, covered with the bark of trees. Every lodge house was provided with open fireplaces, some having as many as a dozen in them. There were large store houses where thousands of bushels of Indian corn were kept. The facades of some of the larger houses, which were often two hundred feet in length, were paneled, and on these panels painted pictures of all sorts of animals and birds. The streets were teeming with life, hunters, trades-people, warriors, housewives, children, all attending to their respective tasks. But no Indian could leave or enter the "castle," as the town was called, without giving the password to the gatekeepers.

The position of gatekeeper was a very honorable one, and was hereditary. On the high ground, where the graveyard was situated, in shady corners of which the ghost-flower grew, all was neatness and precision. The graves were in the shape of mounds, surrounded with small palisades nicely closed up, and painted red, white and black. There were gateways to the graves of the chiefs, on the top of the gates were effigies of large birds, and on the fences were painted all manner of grotesque animals, birds and snakes.

This description of the Oneida Castle at Standing Stone in its hey-day is reminiscent of Arent Van Curler's account of his visit to some of the castles of the same tribe many years later (1634) in Northern New York. The Oneidas, always a superior people, are the only tribe of Indians who successfully adopted the white man's civilization in New York. Their farms are described as veritable garden spots.

But like many cities and races that have a "golden age," a period of decadence fell upon the splendid Oneidas along the Juniata. It was a case of too many blessings. Everybody was prosperous, no one had to worry about making a living. The bounteous Giver of All had showered plenty on his Oneidas.

The cleared fields yielded rich crops of corn, melons, and potatoes, the orchards were laden with apples, plums, persimmons, and the peach, which had been brought from the South. The nut trees were full to overbearing, berries and edible roots were found everywhere. The forests teemed with game, the river with clams, mussels and fish. The seasons were not unkind, there were no blizzards or tornadoes, life was easy, supine.

If the Oneidas had been grateful for all these blessings, fate might have worked kinder for them. But they were far from it, the more they got, the more they wanted. The less they had to work, the less they wanted work. In plain language they wanted to sit under the trees and be fed. They imagined that the universe was created for them, and it wasn't doing all it could for their happiness. They begrudged any time spent in the service of the Power of Nature as expressed in the Gitchie-Manitto. Many of them regarded religious exercises as "foolery" and wondered what they had to be "thankful" for at services of thanksgiving. They looked upon the New Year ceremonies as tiresome, the inscribing of the achievements of the year as superfluous. They were great; they knew it; the Great Spirit, if he existed, must also know it. They were sunk to the lowest depths of spiritual degradation inasmuch as they questioned all things, accepting none.

The leading intellectuals of the castle held numerous secret conclaves with a view of abandoning the New Year ceremonies, so many of the tribesmen were opposed to it. After all, it was only an archaic old pageant; a gay dance with lively music would best usher in the New Year twelve-month. But it took time to overcome a long-established custom, with the memories of centuries clustered about it, and little more than talk came of these meetings of the innovators. Yet each year fewer attended the mystic rites, while on the other hand a society of mummers who held a mock pageant outside the palisades the same day, with wild orgies and rowdy conduct, was becoming yearly more popular, and drew twice the crowds.

A wooden pole painted to imitate the Standing Stone was set up in a cornfield, around which the young bucks and maidens danced. On it were carved all kinds of clownish jests at the sacred language of the real stone. But the Indians liked to laugh, life was sad, it was so easy to live, so hard to die. In secret all had a grudge against the Great Spirit as being the author of death; they felt that there was no other life, consequently hated to let go of the one in hand.

All this time the Great Spirit endured the falling away from grace with extreme patience. In return for agnosticism, neglect, contempt, he handed forth bountiful crops, great catches of fish, mammoth kills of game, equable seasons, freedom from pestilences, long life. Good for evil was bestowed to all, but none were wise enough to take heed.

One evening, shortly before the New Year, an easy-going traveler brought the news to the castle that the bison had arrived in Aughwick Valley. It was late for their fall migration, but it had been a mild autumn, and they lingered longer than usual on their southerly journey. As the grand bison hunt, which usually took place in the latter part of October, "persimmon time," was an annual event of the first magnitude with the Oneidas, as with most of the other tribes in Pennsylvania, there was a skirmishing among the braves to put their spears, lances, and bows in order, to sharpen their celts and skinners. Even the august high priests began to take notice, and talked hunting instead of Standing Stone. The senior priest was detected sharpening his skinning knife, when he should have been preparing his sacred hammer and chisel. If another messenger had not brought news that some members of a tribe from the Susquehanna Valley were already at work slaughtering the bison, the exodus to Aughwick Valley might not have been so general. This was the final straw, every Oneida able to stand the journey broke for the eastern gates with unwonted alacrity, bowling the gate-keepers aside with coarse jests or imprecations. Some were able to procure canoes and barges for the journey, while others rode on hurriedly constructed dog-rafts, or raced along the banks. It was a frenzied, reckless crowd that followed the course of the Juniata that night!

The next day was the first day of the New Year, when the ceremonies at the Standing Stone were always held. The morning dawned clear and cool, without a cloud in the sky, but not a male Oneida except the tiny boys and palsied old men remained in the castle. Many women came out of their houses, assembling in little groups, expressing surprise that the time-honored ceremony was not taking place. But as the day wore on, more of them discussed the prospects of the buffalo hunt than the discarded religious exercises.

Night fell, and the New Year had been ushered in without the pageant, which after all no one missed. A few of the very old feeble Indian braves, too decrepit to leave their cabins, bemoaned the changed order, but they were not worth listening to, so the young folks argued.

At the hunting ground the Oneidas had arrived soon enough to put the marauders from the Susquehanna to rout before they had killed many bison. Before they began the big slaughter, they killed many of the intruding Indians and burned their bodies in a heap. Then they began the butchery, killing the buffaloes right and left. This slaughter continued until they had put an end to all the mature bulls and cows and a goodly proportion of calves. The rest were let go to carry on the race for the next years' hunt. Then came the carnival of skinning, of drying the hides, of curing the meat. It went on while the creek ran red with the drainage from the gory work.

Weeks passed before the last Oneida was back at the castle and took up the thread of the old existence.

The ceremonies at the Standing Stone were forgotten, life went on for a time as if there had never been such a sacred rite. But there soon set in a marked moral deterioration, life without religions could not be otherwise than unmoral. Justice, truth, honor, became misnomers. Disease and degeneracy were everywhere apparent. Pleasure and indolence became the only gods.

Many manly pastimes fell into disrepute, even the chase was considered too great an effort.

It was on the first anniversary of the abandonment of the sacred exercises at the Standing Stone that a terrible pestilence broke out among the Oneidas. It was a vile skin disorder like a leprosy, and no medicine man in the tribe was able to cope with it. The Indians, old and young, "died like flies," yet no one thought to seek divine interference. So great was the power of caste and clannishness that none of the redmen cared to bury the dead. The putrifying corpses lay about in the basilica and alleys, or were piled against the stockades. Vast flocks of buzzards, ravens and other noxious birds feasted off the remains, the air resounding, especially in the night time with their weird cries.

Among the handful of Indians who managed to escape the plague was one very young brave, of no particular elevation of birth, named Wahoorah. Born in an obscure corner of the Juniata country, he somehow or other held firmly to the old ideals and religious practices of his race. He was able to witness the failure of medicine and black art in curing the awful scourge, he saw the danger of the quick extermination of his people, he reasoned out but one cure, a return to the ancient landmarks. Yet his counsels were brushed aside, even by dying men. The course of the tribe was forward, through different channels, the past was dead, the Standing Stone superfluous, all held.

But Wahoorah felt that he had a mission, he must save his race at any cost.

Gathering together a fragment of the tribe, mostly aged men, old women, young women and children, he persuaded them to arrange for the removal of the stone to a new locality to the north. Though he held no official position in the tribe, and was lacking in influential friends, there was no one who interposed any objection to his proposal to carry the stone away.

On the second anniversary of the abandonment of the ancient rites he appeared before the stone, accompanied by his devoted little band. Somewhere he had found the hammer and chisel which the priests of old had used to carve the records of the tribe on the sacred stone. Watched only by his followers, he boldly proceeded to cut the following records on the shaft. First he carved, "Year of the abandonment of the sacred rites. Result: Pestilence, Deterioration, Sorrow." "First anniversary of the abandonment of rites. Death rate growing steadily higher." "Second anniversary, Wahoorah and his followers remove stone to the north."

So absorbed were the tribesmen in their own petty concerns that no one except his followers took the trouble to read the new carvings, which were in hieroglyphic form, the Oneidas having no written language.

After the signs had been placed on the stone, Wahoorah signaled to the most agile of his disciples to pry the stone loose from its foundations. Crowbars and picks were used with a will, with the result that the huge shaft was soon swaying in its gravelly foundations. Wahoorah held the stone in place while his followers got ready to drop it into a net basket in which it was to be dragged overland to the north. While so engaged he failed to notice the approach of the titular chief of the Oneidas, young He-Hu-Ti-Dan. Aroused from a sick bed by the noise in the market place, he had dragged his corruption-covered body to the scene of Wahoorah's activities. With a voice cracked and broken, in a high falsetto key, he ordered the saintly Indian to let the sacred stone alone. His queer voice shrieking from the silence so suddenly caused Wahoorah to turn his head. As he did so his hands slipped and the Standing Stone, loose at its foundations, fell to the earth with a crash and was shattered into a hundred pieces.

This was too much for He-Hu-Ti-Dan. Raising his staff, he sought to smite Wahoorah and send him reeling among the wreckage. But the young warrior dodged the blow, and the chieftain plunged forward, falling in a heap in his long gown like a bag of old bones. There he lay until Wahoorah turned him over on his back, finding him dead. Kicking him out of the way as he would a mass of filth, Wahoorah ordered his followers to gather together the pieces of the sacred stone and place them in the net. Then he told his band that he was ready to start to the north, to a new land; that all who wished to leave behind the enervation and sinfulness of the castle and help carve out a new destiny could do so.

Every member of his party old and young elected to go with him, and toward the mysterious north they wended their way that day at sundown. They had barely disappeared into the blackness of the forest when a band of hardy Tuscaroras from the South entered the castle gates. They had heard of the plight of their relatives, had come to their assistance, bearing supplies and accompanied by wise men and medicine men. They were shocked to find the Standing Stone gone and the town depopulated except for a few sick men. From a dying savage they learned the story of the ravages of the pestilence, of Wahoorah's fruitless efforts to effect a renaissance, of his tragedy and departure. Despite valiant efforts, the proud castle of the Oneidas became a city of the dead in a few days. The medicines and spells of the Tuscaroras availed not, for every Oneida passed away.

The Tuscaroras decided not to remain in the fair valley of the Juniata. They feared they might become afflicted with the foul malady. Thus the site of Standing Stone Town remained untenanted save for the temporary camps of wandering hunters for two centuries. At length a permanent settlement of Tuscaroras was made on the spot, and one of the first acts of these settlers was to hew out a new Standing Stone, to contain their sacred records. With reverent hands it was erected on the site of the ancient stone, and for years it recorded the worthy annals of a noble race. As if to atone for the remissness of their relatives, the Tuscaroras tended this stone most tenderly. And in so doing they won for themselves prosperity and happiness. And they might have remained indefinitely at their beautiful home had it not been for the news of the arrival of a white-skinned race of people in their neighborhood. With this news came a vision to their wisest man, old Pa-Tek-Kwa, that they must remove the stone and migrate to the north. In this vision was portrayed the greatness of the remnant of the Oneidas who had long before followed Wahoorah out of the Juniata country; this destiny would follow the Tuscaroras on their northerly pilgrimage. Abundance would be theirs in the North.

So carefully, fully as carefully as they set it up, the chiefs and wise men took down the Standing Stone, and followed it to the North. In order not to arouse too much curiosity from the white men the stone was taken down at night, and the northerly journey commenced, unlighted even by rays of the moon.

A few days afterward when a party of white surveyors reached the site of the town they were surprised to find it deserted, and strangest of all to find the stone, which they had marked as a "corner" in their notebooks, chief among the missing. But they pitched their camps where the ancient relic had stood, and among themselves resolved to erect another stone in its place as a permanent "corner." One of their number, Andrew Clugage, was able to hew out of the stiff flint a "stone" which seemed the counterpart of its predecessors. And when it was being put in place some wandering Indians appeared on the scene, Indians of venerable mien, who had retentive memories, and they retailed the history of past Standing Stones. And they made the prophecy that as long as a stone stood on the spot and was treated with respect, prosperity and happiness would fall to the lot of all who dwelt near at hand. For was not the first stone the gift of the Gitchie-Manitto himself?

And for some reason there always has been a stone on view at Huntingdon, the Standing Stone Town of romance and history. There is one now in a small public park near the center of the town. Nature has truly lavished all her gifts upon those who have lived near it, prosperity, happiness, contentment, and power have all been dealt out with a bountiful hand, and the old story stretching back into the vistas of dim antiquity has not been forgotten. The historian, the poet, the orator, as well as the humble narrator of legends have all faithfully striven to keep its memory green.

IX.
The Tragic Story of
Pennsylvania's Fountain of Youth

Down through the ages people have dreamed of finding a "Fountain of Youth," a legendary spring or pool of water in which one could bathe to take away the ravages of old age and make one young again. Legends of such a spring or pool of miraculous waters have appeared in almost every culture and period of history. In American history, the famous Spanish explorer and early Governor

of Puerto Rico, Juan Ponce de Leon, is famous for discovering Florida as a result of hearing a story that a such a pool of miraculous waters actually existed somewhere to the north of Puerto Rico.

Yet, while almost every older person dreams of becoming young again, is the recovery of one's youth all that it is cracked up to be in myth and legend? Pennsylvania has a legend that suggests that even if one could find such a fountain of youth and did regain a younger body, the result would be less than satisfying.

This story is intimately connected to the area around Nittany Mountain because, although Wisamek's wife was from Schuylkill county area (Bohundy Creek), the warm springs of which one must first drink before arriving at the fountain of youth are located, according to the legend, in Perry County.

The legend further recounts that when Wisamek, the Indian chief who went to bathe in the waters a second time to restore his youthful mind and spirit (after restoring his youthful body the first time), he left his recent bride to wait for his return at Egg Hill in Penn's Valley, located on the other side of Mount Nittany from Nittany Valley. The area of Egg Hill is almost within sight from the Mount Nittany Inn above Pleasant Gap. Today, Egg Hill is widely known as the location of a famous haunted church.

The Fountain of Youth

Old Chief Wisamek, of the Kittochtinny Indians, had lost his spouse. He was close to sixty years of age, which was old for a redman, especially one who had led the hard life of a warrior, exposed to all kinds of weather, fasts and forced marches. Though he felt terribly lonely and depressed in his state of widowerhood, the thought of discarding the fidelity of the eagle, which, if bereaved, never takes a second mate, and was the noble bird he worshipped, seemed repugnant to him until he happened to see the fair and buxom maid Annapalpeteu.

He was rheumatic, walking with difficulty; he tired easily, was fretful, all sure signs of increasing age; but what upset him most was the sight of his reflection in his favorite pool, a haggard, weazened, wrinkled face, with a nose like the beak of an eagle, and glazed eyes as colorless as clay. When he opened his mouth the reflected image seemed to be mostly toothless, the lips were blue and thin. He had noticed that he did not need to pluck the hairs from his skull any more to give prominence to his warrior's top-knot; the proud tufts itself was growing sparse and weak; to keep it erect he was now compelled to braid it with hair from a buffalo's tail.

Brave warrior that he was, he hated to pay his court to the lovely Annapalpeteu when on all sides he saw stalwart, six-foot youths, masses of sinews and muscle, clear-eyed, firm-lipped, always ambitious and high-spirited, more suited to be her companions.

But one afternoon he saw his copper-colored love sitting by the side of the Bohundy Creek, beating maize in a wooden trough. Her entire costume consisted of a tight petticoat of blue cloth, hardly reaching to the knees, and without any ruffles. Her cheeks and forehead were neatly daubed with red. She seemed very well content with her coadjutor, a bright young fellow, who, except for two wild cat hides appropriately distributed, was quite as naked as the ingenuous beauty. That Annapalpeteau had a cavalier was now certain, and immediately it rankled what flames remained in his jaded body; he must have her at any cost.

Down by the Conadogwinet, across the Broad Mountain, lived Mbison, a wise man. Old Wisamek would go there and consult him, perhaps obtain from him some potion to permanently restore at least a few of the fires of his lost youth. Though his will power had been appreciably slackening of late years, he acted with alacrity on the idea of visiting the soothsayer. Before sundown he was on his way to the south, accompanied by several faithful henchmen. Carrying a long ironwood staff, he moved on with unwonted agility; it was very dark, and the path difficult to follow, when he finally consented to bivouac for the night. The next morning found him so stiff that he could hardly clamber to his feet. His henchmen assisted him, though they begged him to rest for a day. But his will forced him on; he wanted to be verile and win the beautiful Annapalpateu.

The journey, which consumed a week, cost the aged Strephon a world of effort. But as he had been indefatigable in his youth, he was determined to reach the wise man's headquarters walking like a warrior, and not carried there on a litter like an old woman. Bravely he forged ahead, his aching joints paining miserably, until at length he came in sight of his Promised Land.

The soothsayer, who had been apprised of his coming by a dream, was in front of his substantial lodge-house to greet him. Seldom had he received a more distinguished client than Wisamek, so he welcomed him with marked courtesy and deference.

After the first formalities, the old chief, who had restrained himself with difficulty, asked how he could be restored to a youthful condition, so that he could rightfully marry a beautiful maiden of eighteen summers. The wise man, who had encountered similar supplicants in the past, informed him that the task was a comparatively easy one. It would involve, however, first drinking the waters of the Warm Springs (in what is now Perry County), then another journey across mountains.

Wisamek shouted for joy when he heard these words, and impatiently demanded where he would have to go to be finally restored to youth.

"Across many high mountain ranges, across many broad valleys, across many swift streams, through a country covered with dark forests and filled with wild beasts, to the northwest of here, is a wonderful cavern. In it rises a deep stream of greenish color, clear as crystal, the fountain of youth. At its heading you will find a very old man, Gamunk, who knows the formula. Give him this talisman, and he will allow you to bathe in the marvelous waters and be young again."

With the final words he handed Wisamek a red bear's tooth, on which was cleverly carved the form of an athletic youth. The old chief's hands trembled so much that he almost dropped the precious fetich. But he soon recovered his self-control and thanked the wise man. Then he ordered his henchmen to give the soothsayer gifts, which they did, loading him with beads, pottery, wampum and rare furs.

Despite the invitation to remain until he was completely rested, Wisamek determined to depart at once for the warm springs and the fountain of youth. He drank the warm water copiously, enjoying the beautiful surroundings at the springs. He was so stimulated by his high hope and the mineral waters that he climbed the steep ridges, crossed the turbulent streams and put up with the other inconveniences of the long march much better than might have been the case. During the entire journey he sang Indian love songs, strains which had not passed his lips in thirty years.

His followers, gossiping among themselves, declared that he looked better already. Perhaps he would not have to bathe in the fountain after all. He might resume his youth, because he willed it so. Indians were strong believers in the power of mind over matter.

When he reached the vicinity of the cave he was fortunate enough to meet the aged Indian who was its guardian. Though his hair was snow white and he said he was so old that he had lost count of the years, Gamunk's carriage was erect, his complexion smooth, his eyes clear and kindly. He walked along with a swinging stride, very different from Wisamek's mental picture of him. The would-be bridegroom, who handed him the talisman, was quick to impart his mission to his new-found friend.

"It is true," he replied, "after a day and a night's immersion in the cave's water you will emerge with all the appearance of youth. There is absolutely no doubt of it. Thousands have been here before."

With these reassuring words Wisamek again leaped for joy, gyrating like a young brave at a cantico.

The party, accompanied by the old guardian, quickly arrived at the cave's main opening, where beneath them lay stretched the calm, mirror-like expanse of greenish water.

"Can I begin the bath now?" asked the chief, impatiently. "I am anxious to throw off the odious appearance of age."

"Immediately," replied the old watchman, who took him by the hand, leading to the ledge where it was highest above the water. "Jump off here," he said quietly. Wisamek, who had been a great swimmer in his youth and was absolutely fearless of the water, replied that he would do so. "But remember you must remain in the water without food until this hour tomorrow," said the guardian.

As he leaped into the watery depths the chief shouted he would remain twice as long if he could be young again. Wisamek was true to his instructions; there was too much at stake; he dared not falter.

The next morning his henchmen were at the cave's mouth to greet his reappearance. They were startled to see, climbing up the ledge with alacrity, a tall and handsome man, as young looking as themselves. There was a smile on the full, red lips, a twinkle in the clear eye of the re-made warrior as he stood among them, physically a prince among men.

The homeward journey was made with rapidity. Wisamek traveled so fast that he played out his henchmen who were half his age.

Annapalpeteu, who was seated in front of her parents' cabin weaving a garment, noticed a youth of great physical beauty approaching, at the head of Chief Wisamek's clansmen. She wondered who he could be, as he wore Wisamek's headdress of feathers of the osprey or "sea eagle." When he drew near he saluted her, and, not giving her time to answer, joyfully shouted: "Don't you recognize me? I am your good friend Wisamek, come back to win your love, after a refreshing journey through the distant forests."

Annapalpeteu, who was a sensible enough girl to have admired the great warrior for his prowess, even though she had never thought of him seriously as a lover, was now instantly smitten by his engaging appearance. The henchmen withdrew, leaving the couple together. They made marked progress with their romance; words of love were mentioned before they parted.

It was not long before the betrothal was announced, followed shortly by the wedding festival. At the nuptials the bridegroom's appearance was the marvel of all present. It was hinted that he had been somewhere and renewed his youth, but as the henchmen were sworn to secrecy, how it had been done was not revealed.

The young bride seemed radiantly happy. She had every reason to be; the other Indian maids whispered from lip to lip, was she not marrying the greatest warrior and hunter of his generation, the handsomest man in a hundred tribes? Secretly envied by all of her age, possessing her stalwart prize, the fair bride started on her honeymoon, showered with acorns and good wishes.

So far as is known the wedding trip passed off blissfully. There were smiles on the bright faces of both bride and groom when they returned to their spacious new lodge-house, which the tribe had erected for them in their absence, by the banks of the sparkling Bohundy. But the course of life did not run smoothly for the pair. Though outwardly Wisamek was the handsomest and most youthful-looking of men, he was still an old man at heart. Annapalpeteu was as pleasure-loving as she was beautiful. She wanted to dance and sing and mingle with youthful company. She wanted her good time in life; her joy of living was at its height, her sense of enjoyment at its zenith.

On the other hand, Wisamek hated all forms of gaieties or youthful amusements. He wanted to sit about the lodge-house in the sun, telling of his warlike triumphs of other days; he wanted to sleep much, he hated noise and excitement.

Annapalpeteu, dutiful wife that she was, tried to please him, but in due course of time both husband and wife realized that romance was dying, that they were drifting apart. Wisamek was even more aware of it than his wife. It worried him greatly, his dreams were of an unhappy nature. He pictured the end of the trail, with his wife, Annapalpeteu, in love with some one else of her own age, some one whose heart was young. He had spells of moodiness and irritability, as well as several serious quarrels with his wife, whom he accused of caring less for him than formerly.

The relations became so strained that life in the commodious lodge-house was unbearable. At length it occurred to Wisamek that he might again visit the fountain of youth, this time to revive his soul. Perhaps he had not remained in the water long enough to touch the spirit within. He informed his spouse that he was going on a long journey on invitation of the war chief of a distant tribe, and that she must accompany him. He was insanely jealous of her now. He could not bear her out of his sight. He imagined she had a young lover back of every tree, though she was honor personified.

The trip was made pleasantly enough, as the husband was in better spirits than usual. Annapalpeteu enjoyed the waters of the warm springs, would liked to have tarried. He thought he saw the surcease of his troubles ahead of him!

When he reached the Beaver Dam Meadows, at the foot of Egg Hill, near the site of the present town of Spring Mills, beautiful level flats which in those days were a favorite camping ground for the red men, he requested the beautiful Annapalpeteu to remain there for a few days, that he was going through a hostile country, he would not jeopardize her safety. He was going on an important mission that would make her love him more than ever when he returned. In reality no unfriendly Indians were about, but in order to give a look of truth to his story he left her in charge of a strong bodyguard.

Wisamek's conduct of late had been so peculiar that his wife was not sorry to see her lord and master go away. Handsome though he was, a spiritual barrier had arisen between them which grew more insurmountable with each succeeding day. Yet, on this occasion, when he was out of her sight, she felt apprehensive about him. She had a strange presentiment that she would never see him again.

Wisamek was filled with hopes; his spirits had never been higher, as he strode along, followed by his henchmen. When he reached the top of the path which led to the mouth of the enchanted cave, he met old Gamunk, the guardian. The aged redman expressed surprise at seeing him again.

"I have come for a very peculiar reason," he said. "The bath which I took last year outwardly made me young, but only outwardly. Within I am as withered and joyless as a centenarian. I want to bathe once more, to try to revive the old light in my soul."

Gamunk shook his head. "You may succeed; I hope you will. I never heard of any one daring to take a second bath in these waters. The tradition of the hereditary guardians, of whom I am the hundredth in direct succession, has it that it would be fatal to take a second immersion, especially to remain in the water for twenty-four hours."

Then he asked Wisamek for the talisman which gave him the right to bathe. Wisamek drew himself up proudly, and, with a gesture of his hand indicating disdain, said he had no talisman, that he would bathe anyhow. He advanced to the brink and plunged in. Until the same hour the next day he floated and paddled about the greenish depths, filled with expectancy. For some reason it seemed longer this time than on the previous visit.

At last, by the light which filtered down through the treetops at the cave's mouth, he knew that the hour had come for him to emerge—emerge as Chief Wisamek—young in heart as in body. Proudly he grasped the rocky ledge and swung himself out on dry land. He arose to his feet. His head seemed very light and giddy. He fancied he saw visions of his old conquests, old loves. There was the sound of music in the air.

Was it the martial drums, played to welcome the conqueror, or the wind surging through the feathery tops of the maple and linden trees at the mouth of the cave? He started to climb the steep path. He seemed to be treading the air. Was it the buoyant steps of youth come again? He seemed to float rather than walk. The sunlight blinded his eyes. Suddenly he had a flash of normal consciousness. He dropped to the ground with a thud like an old pine falling. Then all was blackness, silence. Jaybirds complaining in the treetops alone broke the stillness.

His bodyguards, who were waiting for him at old Gamunk's lodge-house, close to where the hotel now stands, became impatient at his non-appearance, as the hour was past. Accompanied by the venerable watchman they started down the path. To their horror they saw the dead body of a hideous, wrinkled old man, all skin and bones, like a desiccated mummy, lying stretched out across it, a few steps from the entrance to the cave. When they approached closely they noticed several familiar tattoo marks on the forehead, which identified the body as that of their late master, Wisamek.

Frightened lest they would be accused of his murder, and shocked by his altered appearance, the bodyguards turned and took to their heels. They disappeared in the trackless forests to the north and were never seen again.

Old Gamunk, out of pity for the vain-glorious chieftain, buried the remains by the path near where he fell. As for poor Annapalpeteu, the beautiful, she waited patiently for many days by the Beaver Dam, but her waiting was in vain. At length, concluding that he had been slain in battle in some valorous encounter, she started for her old home on the Bohundy.

It is related that on the way she met and married a warrior of her own age, living happily ever afterwards in a comfortable cabin somewhere in the majestic Bower Mountains. In him she found the loving response, the congeniality of pleasures which had been denied the dried, feeble soul of Wisamek, who bathed too often in the fountain of youth.

X.
Stories with Lessons from Beyond Our Area

This following two stories are the exception to the geographic plan of this book, i.e., to include legends and stories relating only to the area within the magically mythical area bounded by Bald Eagle Creek on the west, the West Branch of the Susquehanna on the north, the Susquehanna River on the east, and the Juniata River on the south.

The first story of "Why the Seneca Would Not Eat Trout" is told some twelve miles north of the West Branch of the Susquehanna, along the Coudersport Pike in Lycoming County. But its moral seems so relevant to modern life that it simply begs to be included. The moral: great wealth and success leads to immorality. The Seneca believed that those of their ancestors who had given in to a life of immorality and drunkenness had been turned into trout by the Gitchie Manitou, and that the speckles on the trout recorded their sins.

The second story, "Poplar George," takes place along the Pucketa river in Westmoreland County. In this editor's opinion, it is one to send chills down the spine of any active outdoorsman with an over-active imagination. I have taken an axe or saw to several trees in my life. But after reading this story I can never do so again without thinking: "What if there is some spirit in this tree whose legs I am sawing off?" "What if this tree is alive, and I am hacking at its legs?"

One does not have to be an environmentalist to believe that there is a spirit or soul in every living thing, and to be very careful of offending it...

Why the Seneca Would Not Eat Trout

The Indians had finished setting potatoes on the Fenster-macker place and had gathered at the old farmhouse for supper. It was a cold, bleak day, although past the middle part of May.

Very few blossoms were out, as the season on the mountain top was said to be two weeks behind that in the valleys. The farm occupied a bare space hewed out of the ancient forest on a high plateau, with the higher mountains of the Black Forest surrounding it on all sides. Several trout-fishermen from Williamsport were spending the night at the farmhouse, and the good wife had kindly consented to cook a "mess" of their fish for supper. They were small, puny trout to be sure, but the city fishermen could not have been prouder of them had they all been over a foot in length.

"It looks like harvest time," remarked old Daddy Fenstermaker, as he stared about at the dozen faces assembled at the long table, when he had finished saying "Grace."

The six Indians were a stolid, unimaginative looking crew, dregs of the proud race of the Senecas, once the rulers of Northern Pennsylvania. They presented an unkempt contrast to the short-haired sportsmen with their cropped mustaches, their spectacles and tweed suits, and even to old man Fenstermaker himself. For the sake of politeness the fishermen passed the big dish containing the trout to the Indians, but they declined the fish, one after another. The fishermen thought at first that it was because the Indians feared to deprive them of some of the results of their outing, and urged them to take some, and one went so far as to remark jokingly that Indians doubtless preferred bigger trout.

The situation required some explanation, so Daddy Fenstermaker spoke up and said that members of the Seneca tribe never ate trout. "I don't know why it is," he continued, "but no Indian who ever worked for me would touch a trout; perhaps some one here can tell the gentlemen the reason?"

There was a moment's silence and then Billy Shongo, the brightest looking of the Indians ventured to say that his people were a queer lot, that if he was doing the right thing, he could not be even engaged in farm work. "One of our wise men, in advising us to keep out of farming put it in this way, 'You ask me to plow the ground! Shall I take a knife and tear my mother's bosom? Then when I die she will not take me to her bosom to rest. You ask me to grub out stones! Shall I dig under her skin for bones? Then when I die I cannot enter her body to be born again. You ask me to cut grass and make hay and sell it, and be rich like white men! But how dare I cut off my mother's hair?'"

"That reminds me of Chief Red Jacket's indignant reply to the request that he sell land, 'Why not sell the sea, the air and the sky'" said one of the fishermen.

"We have violated all this and more, but very few of us have eaten any trout," Shongo continued impressively.

All of us including the fishermen urged the Seneca to tell us why his tribe would not eat trout. To us they seemed to be the sweetest and cleanest of all fish. "All right, I'll tell you, but please excuse me if I detain you too long."

"Go on, go on," said almost everybody, so Shongo commenced his story.

"It was long, long ago, when this world was new, and the Senecas were the chosen people of the Great Spirit. In those days the Indians lived along the banks of the big rivers such as the Allegheny, the Genesee, and the Susquehanna. There were broad flats on both sides of the banks where they raised corn, sweet potatoes, muskmelons, and where their orchards were located. Some Indians owned orchards which covered over a thousand acres, all planted with the best apple, peach, and plum trees. In those days, the Indians gave all their attention to farming, and gave little time to hunting. They sometimes shot water birds, which flew along the rivers, or sieved with their bark nets, the fine shad, salmon, and other river fish. They never visited the mountain streams which were said to be alive with serpents, allies of the evil One.

"But farming brought them into evil ways. The democracy of the hunting camps could not exist among them. Some became very rich and powerful, and the sons and daughters of these were proud, arrogant and cruel. As they rose in the social scale they forced their less fortunate fellow beings who did the real work into a state bordering on slavery. The wealthy ones thought only of pleasure. They desired no offspring. They invented queer dances, copied from the antics of the beasts and birds of the woods, and at these they indulged themselves all night long, and slept by day. All kinds of vice and crime thrived among these idlers. The only religious rites they cared for were those where human sacrifices were made, and they gloated, and laughed and sang lewd songs while the victims were being tortured horribly. They would not speak to the Indians of the coarser sort, and boasted loudly about 'divine right,' a 'ruling class' and the like.

"Among themselves they were not one whit less mean. They robbed and plundered one another when they could, they were jealous and envious to the last degree. But their immoralities were the worst part of them. First of all whenever they saw a beautiful young girl in the home of one of their slaves, they stole her away, toyed with her a while, and when they saw a prettier or fresher one, they had the predecessor put to death by slow torture. Some wicked Indians of the lower classes sold their daughters as playthings for the rich. Then they got to stealing one-another's wives. In some of their orgies, when steeped with a corn liquor which they distilled, they exchanged wives. Love was reduced to commercialism and lust, and all the higher, finer impulses, such as the Great Spirit willed the Senecas to possess were dead.

"All this was about two thousand years ago or more. I am glad it was so long ago, that we can almost imagine that it was a myth." We say to our young people that such doings were exaggerated, but in our hearts we know that it was all only too true. From his home among the clouds, above the tallest mountains, the Great Spirit viewed the state of affairs with growing concern. He loved the Senecas above all of his other creations, and it grieved him to see their degeneracy. He breathed his soul deeply into some wise men and sent them among the rich as teachers. But when they had been laughed to scorn, the Master Mind realized that he must adopt more drastic measures.

"The rich people were so imbued with their own importance that they must be shocked into a sense of right. He sent horrible new diseases among them, cutting down the powerful, the young, and beautiful. The dancing groves became burial places. There were so many dead to lay away. But with the nearness of the death the Indians resolved to 'have a good time while life lasted' and plunged deeper into foul lasciviousness. They did not mind death if they could extract the last ounce of pleasure from life while it lasted. The Great Spirit delayed his vengeance. His divine pressure produced such slight results that he began to doubt his omnipotence. But as matters were steadily growing worse, he launched his final thunderbolt. The idle rich had planned a great outdoor dance carnival. Like beasts they were to dance all the new steps scantily clad, and then feast and drink until they fell to the earth from the excess of pleasure.

"A level plain, shaded by tall, hardwood trees was selected as the place for the orgy. Once it had been a pasture ground for buffaloes and elks, but the animals had moved into other localities and it had become overgrown with trees and brush. The undergrowth was cut away, so that the vast area presented a park-like appearance. On the edges of this park, where the old forest was dense, hearths and pits were constructed to roast the whole carcasses of animals, such as moose, elks, and buffaloes. Many new dance steps were invented for the occasion, and the entertainment began with human sacrifices. Fifty beautiful young girls of the poorer class were tortured to death to arouse the jaded instincts of the pleasure-seekers.

"Then the dancing began, it was to last until hunger overcame the revellers, then they were to gorge themselves into insensibility with the elaborate repast provided. The Great Spirit viewed these arrangements with disgust, and made ready for his retribution. The ungrateful beings had perverted his lofty purpose in placing them in the world, they had made his image a silly mockery. The sun was shining brightly when the exercises commenced, and the groans of the dying girls drowned out a breeze which had sprung up among the feathery tops of the tall hardwoods.

"Just as the Indian players struck up the first weird notes of the dance music the clouds darkened, and there were several deafening peals of thunder. Some few of the more delicately nurtured were for dropping out of the dances, and running to the more sheltered woods or caves, but the leaders of the entertainment who believed in pleasure at any cost shouted ' on with the dance, it will be a new sensation to dance with the water dripping down our backs. So the dance proceeded, many reasoning out that the thunder and lightning only portended a passing shower. But when the rain fell, the Heavens literally opened, and soon the level plain was indented with water courses. The amazed dancers strove to keep their feet, but the heavy downpour literally laid them low. They sprawled all over on the muddy earth, and some tried to roll to places of safety. Many fell into the water courses and were swept away in the brown, grimy torrents.

"Those who rolled over the ground experienced a peculiar sensation. They felt slimy like fish, their hands and feet congealed to the shape of fins, great gaping gills appeared in the corners of their throats. They felt themselves diminishing in size. As they struck the water, they felt the horrible obsession that they were fish. Struggle they could not, was it all a dream, produced by superabundant pleasure, or had they been seized with another new disease? If so, their lofty position in the world's social scale would soon lessen it for them; they believed that they never suffered as acutely as the plainer sort. But on this occasion they ceased to be the petted darlings of infinity; they were fish, and for all time. The rain or whatever it was continued until the last member of the wealthy class had been washed into the new-formed streams and transformed into fish.

"Then the sky suddenly became light, and the muddy water-courses transparent mountain brooks. In these brooks swam myriads of handsome, speckled fish. The spots, we were told, corresponded with the number of sins committed by the creatures while in human form. We were ordered never to eat a spotted fish, as it would mean accepting another's sins. The spotted fish soon accustomed themselves to their new environment, and began recognizing old friends. Life might have been quite pleasant in the cool, shaded brooks, only they found that when they attempted to speak water ran into their throats enough to choke them. Those who uttered a single word perished miserably, and came to the surface, and floated with white-stomachs up-wards. They polluted the habitations of the survivors, so few attempted to open their mouths except to breathe and take in nourishment.

"No sooner had they begun to adjust themselves to this situation when a fresh peril appeared. From under logs and stobs which lay in the streams issued an army of hideous, brown serpents, water snakes. They emerged so suddenly that the frightened trout had not time to turn around. Great numbers were partially swallowed, horribly bitten, and disgorged by the slimy monsters. Others were completely eaten, distending the sides of their devourers. The fish became panic-stricken, and swam hither and thither, some even throwing themselves on the banks, where they could not get their breaths, dying there and becoming food for small animals, flies and bugs.

"The most sagacious fish managed to exist somehow. But they knew no peace, by day or night. They were ever on the alert to escape the rapacious water-snakes. Even their spawn or young were devoured by the millions. A fresh enemy, though on a smaller scale, green frogs, assailed them in quarters where the snakes seldom visited. These creatures were particularly destructive of the fry or small fish, as well as of the spawn. Despite their lowly position the erstwhile pleasure-seekers now felt a desire to carry on their race; their normal instincts returned with their metamorphosis. Formerly they had ben evolved to a point too high for their own good; a check was needed. Perhaps their punishment was only temporary, but as time wore on there was no sign that there would be a change. And worst of all, not a single trout died a natural death. As they grew older and weaker, they were devoured by the water snakes, or even by frogs, lizards or eels, passing away mutilated and miserably.

"But they found that they had a guardian angel, the Great Blue Heron. This bird was the sworn enemy of the water snakes and frogs. It hunted them with the same avidity as the snakes pursued the fish. And many a six foot snake slid down the long throats of the herons. And as new generations of fish were born they came to regard the herons as their divinities. But all the same, the old, weak, fish were regularly eaten by the serpents, as there were never enough herons to diminish the number of snakes appreciably. It was a horrible destiny, but it was warranted by the hideous lives which the spotted fish had lived while in human form. But a still more horrible fate was in store.

"A few Indians had escaped from the dreadful flood. They were mostly of the baser sort, who had shunned agriculture, and lived by the chase, and on berries and roots, in the deep forests. These were joined by a few survivors of the dance orgy, who were near to the edges of the big timber when the storm broke, and who rushed pell-mell into the forest depths, escaping being swept into the streams. These had a chance to note what had happened, and informed the other Indians whom they later met, who dwelt in the inmost recesses of the forests. And that was why when they assembled at the banks of the streams, which were swimming full of speckled trout, they refrained from catching or eating them. Their wise men told them that they would become responsible for the sins of the fishes' ancestors of they touched them. And they accepted it as fact.

"For centuries the Senecas never tasted trout, and the streams in Northern Pennsylvania fairly teemed with them. They were polluted, tainted food, while the spots or sins showed out on them. But the redmen loved the clean, pure river fish, and were experts in netting and snaring them. Also they kept their hands off farming, it had been the cause of the terrible downfall of the others. But all was different when the white men came. They did not stop to inquire if the Indians ate trout or not. They started to catch the 'speckled beauties' with their hands, then with hooks and nets, and when they could not get them fast enough these ways, they placed dynamite in the creeks. The fish, who knew the story of their unhappy origin, it was somehow handed down to each new generation, shrank with horror from being hooked and seined by white beings, in form though not in color, as they themselves had been. And they even had to gaze upon the destruction of their divinities, the herons.

"The misguided fishermen attacked the heronries, calling the poor birds 'enemies of the fish,' and slaughtered them without quarter. The water snakes increased in numbers, likewise the frogs; it became harder for the trout to exist. Lumber mills, which dumped unwholesome sawdust into the streams, sprang up on all sides, and later on, tanneries and acid factories poured rank poisons into every water course. It seemed as if the final fate of the cursed trout was to be their worst. The poisons produced loathsome sores and corruptions on their spotted sides, they actually rotted to death.

"But the fish laws made still more suffering for them. When trout less than six inches in length were caught, the law compelled the white sportsmen to throw them back into the water. But the touch of human fingers was an added curse. It produced on every small fish, thus given his freedom, cancers and foul sores worse than the poisons had created. The fish sloughed away, dying hideously, or being easily captured by the snakes in their weakened condition. Man's final blight was more than they had ever dreamed could come to them. Now, you know why the Senecas will never eat trout."

It was pitchy dark in the little dining room when Billy Shongo finished his narrative. The supper things still remained on the table, in front of all of us, and several full cups of coffee were untasted. The good wife and the hired girl sat open-mouthed on chairs, too much interested to clear off the table, or to bring in the lamp. The fire in the little wood-stove between the windows had burned down to a grey ash. The room had become uncomfortably cold. But we had heard a tragic story, and were well recompensed.

"How strange it is," said one of the prosperous looking fishermen, "that we are out here as agents to wreak a further punishment on those fish; why I must have thrown back fifty trout this morning for being undersize. I feel like swearing off trout-fishing."

His companions laughed, and then everybody got up and went into the roomy kitchen adjoining where it was warmer. The Indians went out on the porch, and leaned against the wooden uprights, their instinct seemed to always take them into the open. We could hear a sheep-bell tinkling in the nearby barnyard. Down in the swamp, the "peepers" were chorusing shrilly. We listened to them awhile.

Then Billy Shongo spoke again. "Even those little creatures eat lots of young trout at certain seasons of the year. I don't see how the fish can survive with so many enemies. Man, instead of protecting them, is making it harder for them to exist every year. But I'm thankful that the herons are to be protected again. It is silly to kill them and let water snakes live. But then we can never understand the white man's ways."

Poplar George

"I have been reading your legends of the old days in the 'North American'," said the delegate to the Grange Convention, stroking his long silky mustache, "and they remind me of many stories that my mother used to tell me when I was a little shaver, while we were living on the Pucketa, in Westmoreland County. There was one story that I used to like best of all. It was not the one about old Pucketa the Indian warrior for whom the run was named, but about a less notable Indian, but more esteemed locally, known as 'Poplar George.'"

"It isn't nearly as interesting an Indian story as the one that Emerson Collins tells, of the time when his mother, as a little girl on the Quinneshockeny, went to the spring for a jug of water, finding a lone Indian sitting there all by himself, looking as if he was in deep thought. As he made no move to molest her, she filled her jug, and then scampered hack to the house as fast as she could tote the jug there.

"She was a little shy about telling of her strange experience, but finally, when she mentioned the subject, her mother said, 'maybe the poor fellow was hungry.' Quickly spreading a 'piece,' she hurried back to the spring, but no Indian was to be found, only a few prints of his mocassined feet in the soft earth by the water course. If it hadn't been for those footprints she would have always felt that she had not seen a real live Indian, but a ghost.

"It was the last Indian ever heard of on the Quinneshockeny, and he had probably come back to revive old memories of his happy childhood. No, Poplar George was hardy like Emerson Collins' 'last Indian,' as he, my mother averred, was part Indian, part ghost. He was also the last Indian that ever visited the Pucketa, which had been a famous stream in its day for redmen, from the time when old Pucketa, himself, came there to spend his last days, after having been driven out from his former hunting grounds at the head of Lost Creek, which runs into the 'Blue Juniata' above Mifflintown.

"The principal part of this story revolves around two large trees that used to stand near the Pucketa, one a big tulip or 'whitewood' tree, hollow at the butt, so much so that a half grown person could hide in it, and a huge water poplar tree, or 'cottonwood,' a rare tree in Pennsylvania, you know, that stood on lower ground directly in line wath it, but on the far side of the creek, which ran parallel with the road. It wasn't much of a road in those days, I'm told, isn't much of one yet, little better than a cow path, with grass and dandelions growing between the wagon tracks, and a worn foot-path on the creek side of it. Many's the time I've gone along that path to and from school, or to fetch the cows.

"In my boyhood there were two big stumps which always arrested my attention, the stumps of the 'cottonwood' and the tulip which I have already mentioned. The native poplar stump, which was chopped breast high for some reason, had been cut before my day, but the tulip tree had stood a dead stab for many years, and was not finally cut until my babyhood. I was too young to recall it, and its stump had been sawed off almost level with the ground.

"When my mother was old enough to notice things, say along six, or seven or eight years of age, both trees was standing, and despite their venerable age, were thrifty and green; the hollow trunk of the tulip did not seem to lessen its vitality. Trees in those days, of all kinds, were pretty common, and regarded as nuisances; the farmers were still having 'burning bees' in the spring and fall when all hands would join in and drag with ox-spans the logs of the trees that had been cut when they were clearing new ground, and making huge bonfires, burn them like a modern section foreman does a pile of old railroad ties, and by the way, the time is going to come soon when tie burners will be as severely condemned as the instigators of the 'burning bees' in the olden days.

"Trees were too plentiful to attract much attention or create affection or veneration, but these two trees had a very special human interest.

"Long after the Indians passed out of our country they came back as ghosts or 'familiars,' just as the wolves, panthers and wild pigeons do, so that the stories of folks seeing them after they became extinct, while not literally true, are in a sense correct. Closely associated with the life of the big cottonwood was an old Indian, mother said; he wasn't a real live Indian, yet not a ghost, was probably a half ghost, half Indian, if there could be any such thing.

"The tulip tree was inhabited by a very attractive spirit, an Indian girl, an odd looking one too, for her smooth skin was only a pumpkin color and her eyes a light blue. They all called her 'Pale Eyes,' and she was described as slight, winsome and wonderfully pretty. The Indian man, because he spent so much time under the cottonwood or water poplar, became generally known as 'Poplar George.' He would appear in the neighborhood early in the spring, in time to gather poke, milkweed, dandelion and bracken for the farmer's wives, and to teach the young folks to fish, to use the bow and arrow, and snare wild pigeons and doves.

"It was a sure sign of spring when the young people would see him squatting before a very small fire of twigs under the still leafless branches of the ancient poplar tree. He would remain about all summer long, helping with the harvest, so he must have been real flesh and blood, in a sense, and in the fall he gathered nuts, and later cut some cordwood for those who favored him—but in truth he never liked hard, downright work overly much.

"He was a creature of the forests and streams. When he went away in the fall, after the wild pigeons had left, he always said that he wintered south, on the Casselman River, where the weather was not so severe, in that wonderful realm of the Pawpaw, the Persimmon and the Red Bud.

"Often when he took the young folks of the neighborhood on fishing trips, and his skill with the angle and fly were unerring, the pretty Indian maiden, 'Pale Eyes,' would turn up, and be with the party all day. When asked who she was, he would sometimes say that she was his daughter, other times his niece, or grand-daughter, but when anyone asked of 'Pale Eyes,' she would shake her pretty head, indicating that she only spoke the Indian language. Poplar George could speak Dutch and a little English.

"No one knew where Poplar George slept, if it wasn't in the open, under the cottonwood tree. If he slept in barns, or under haystacks, no one had ever seen him coming or going, but a detail like that, mattered nothing as long as he was kindly and harmless, and took good care of the children.

"He was a master of woodcraft, much like that old Narragansett Indian 'Nessmuk,' who furnished the late George W. Sears with his inspiration as well as 'nom de plume.' Poplar George could call the wild birds off the trees, so that they would feed on the ground before him, the squirrels and even the shy chipmunks climbed all over him, and extracted nuts from his pockets.

"The old Indian was an odd person to look at, so my mother said; of medium height, meagre, wrinkled and weazened, tobacco colored, with little black shoe-button eyes, and a sparse mustache and beard. He dressed in rags, and was often bare-footed, yet he never complained of the cold. He was always jolly and cheerful, had always been the same; he had been coming to the Pucketa Valley for several generations before my mother's day; in fact, no one could remember when he hadn't been there, but that wasn't saying much, as it was a new country, dating only from the time when Pucketa and his tribesmen had enjoyed it as a hunting ground for big game.

"Once when some hunters killed a bear, they were going to nail the paws on the end of a log barn, but Poplar George begged for them, and invited the children to a feast of 'bear paw cutlets' under the Cottonwood tree. My mother sat beside 'Pale Eyes,' and took a great fancy to her; she was able to talk with her in sign language, and Poplar George, seeing how well they got on together, occasionally interpreted for them.

"Mother managed to learn that 'Pale Eyes'' abode was in a huge hollow tulip tree, but that she, too, wintered in the south, but beyond the Maryland line. Those were all gloriously care-free, happy days, and my mother, in later life, never tired talking about them.

"Once in the fall when the buckwheat harvest was in progress, millions of wild pigeons came in, and mother could never forget the sight of old Poplar George sitting on a 'stake and rider' fence, with a handsome cock pigeon resplendent with its ruddy breast, pearched on one of his wrists, while it pecked at some buckwheat seeds in his other hand. Beside him sat the demure 'Pale Eyes,' a speckled squab of the year in her lap, stroking it, while other pigeons, usually so wild, were feeding in the stubble about them, or perched on the stakes of the fence.

"Some of the boys of sixteen years or thereabouts, grown lads they seemed to my mother, wanted to be attentive to 'Pale Eyes,' but she was so shy that she never let them get close to her. As it was a respectable backwoods community, and all minded their own business, no further efforts were made to have her mingle in society.

"There was a rich boy, Herbert Hiltzheimer from Philadelphia, whose father was a great land owner, and who sometimes came with his parents to stay with their Agent while inspecting their possessions, who, at first sight of 'Pale Eyes,' fell violently in love with her. On rainy days he was not allowed out of doors, and sent word to Poplar George that 'Pale Eyes' should go to the Agent's house, and play with him. Old Poplar George replied that he was willing if his niece would consent, but she always ran away into the depths of the forest, and was never once induced to play with him indoors. She did not dislike the city boy, only was very timid, and was afraid to go inside of a house.

"My mother was made a confidante of by Herbert, who offered her five dollars, a colossal sum in those days, if she would induce 'Pale Eyes' to at least come into the Agent's yard, and play with him alone. He had her name cut on everything, even on the window frames, and wrote verses about her which he carried in his pocket, and sometimes tried to read to her.

"In the fall he was taken back to Philadelphia to school, but said that, the evening before, when he walked up the lane, weeping over his misfortune, he opportunately met the fair Indian maid alone at the tulip tree, and actually kissed her. She broke away and ran into the hollow trunk, and while he quickly followed her into the aperture, she had disappeared.

"The lands on which the cottonwood and the tulip tree stood were a part of a farm belonging to 'Squire George Garnice, an agreeable, but easy going old gentleman, who never learned to say 'no' to any one, though not much to his detriment for he was very generally respected.

"One fall some of the Fiedler boys suggested to him, that he let them go on his property and cut up a lot of old half-dead

213

good-for-nothing trees for cordwood and of course he assented. The first tree they attacked was Poplar George's favorite, the mighty cottonwood. They were skilled axemen, and cut a level stump but too high for these days of conservation. Soon the big poplar was down, and the boys were trimming off the sweeping branches. Before cutting into stove lengths, they hopped across the creek and started on their next victim, the hollow tulip tree, the home of 'Pale Eyes.'

"One of the boys, the youngest, Ed, had gotten a new cross-cut saw, and begged them to try it on the tulip. They notched, and then getting down on their knees, started to saw a low stump, for some reason or other. They had sawed in quite a distance on both edges of the hollow side when they heard a piteous shrieking and wailing down the road, toward the old 'Squire's barn.

"Leaving saw, axes and wedges, they ran to where the cries came from, and to their horror, found 'Pale Eyes' lying on the grassy bank beside the road at the orchard, her ankles terribly lacerated, front and back, clear in to the bones, and bleeding profusely. On this occasion she was able to speak in an intelligible tongue.

"'Run quick to the 'Squire's, and get help,' she said, in Pennsylvania German; 'I am dying, but I want something to ease this dreadful pain.'

"The sympathetic boys, without waiting to inquire where she received her grievous hurts, scurried down the road and through the 'Squire's gate. The old gentleman was in his library, drawing up a legal document, when the long, lanky youths, hatless and breathless, burst in on him.

"'Oh, sir,' they chorused, 'the Indian girl. 'Pale Eyes,' you know, has cut herself, and is dying up the road, and wants help.'

"The 'Squire always kept an old-fashioned remedy chest in his desk, so seizing it, and adjusting his curly wig, so that it would not blow off, he ran out after the nimble mountaineers. As they left the gate they saw old Poplar George running across the orchard in the direction of the wounded girl. Evidently he, too, had heard her cries.

"When they reached the spot where marks on the greensward showed where 'Pale Eyes' had been lying, she was nowhere to be found, neither was Poplar George. There were no signs of blood, only a lot of sawdust like comes from the workings of a cross-cut saw.

"The old 'Squire was nonplussed, but consented to accompany the boys to the scene of their wood cutting operations. 'Pale Eyes' was not there either, nor Poplar George. The newly formed leaves of the Cottonwood—it was in the month of May—although the tree had only been cut and sawed into but an hour before, were scorched and withered.

"The 'Squire showed by his face how heartbroken he was to see the two picturesque trees so roughly treated, but he was too kindly and forgiving to chide the boys for their sake. As he was standing there, looking at the ruin, a number of school children, among them my mother, came along, for it was during the noon recess, or dinner hour. They saw the butchered trees, and learned of the events of the morning; several of them, prosaic backwoods youngsters, though they were, shed bitter tears.

"'Dry your eyes.' the 'Squire urged them, 'else your people will think that the teacher licked you.' Then they all chorused that it was a shame to have ruined the retreats of Poplar George and 'Pale Eyes.'

"Evidently 'Squire Garnice was wise in the lore of mysticism, for he shook his head sadly, saying, 'Never mind, you'll never see Poplar George nor 'Pale Eyes' again.'

"It was a dejected company that parted with him at his gate. The old 'Squire was right, for never more was anything seen or heard of Poplar George and the mysterious 'Pale Eyes.' They must have been in some unknowable way connected with the lives of those two trees, the cottonwood and the tulip—their lives or spirits maybe, and when they were cut into, their spirits went out with them.

"I knew of a wealthy man who had a cedar tree in his yard, that when he fell ill, the tree became brown, but retained a little life. Finally it was cut down as an eyesore, and the gentleman died suddenly a few days afterward. That tree must have contained a vital part of his spirit.

"By fall the tulip tree looked as if it had been dead for years, and the bark was peeling off. As the wood of the poplar would not burn, and set up a fetid odor, the Fieldler boys never bothered to finish cutting down the hollow tulip tree, of which the shy wood sprite, 'Pale Eyes,' had been the essence.

"Much of the mystery and charm of that old grass-grown way along the gently flowing Pucketa had vanished with its Indian frequenters. But the memory of Poplar George and 'Pale Eyes' will never be forgotten as long as any of those children who were lucky enough to know them, remain in this world."

An Invitation to Adventurers to the Sites of *The Legends of the Nittany Valley*

The legendary history of the Nittany Valley is the story of spirit across generations. In these stories lies a cultural heritage common to all who enter into the shadow of Mount Nittany. And as beautiful as these stories are to *read*, they're even more wondrous to experience. The scene of action in each takes place in a real, physical place—places *you* can visit.

An afternoon hike up Mount Nittany. Unexpectedly catching a majestic sunrise over Happy Valley. A moment of admiration for the sheer wonder of campus as you linger on the Mall under the few remaining Elms. These are experiences known to countless Penn Staters, townspeople, and visitors. They're experiences that touch the heart; that linger in the soul for years to come. They're pilgrimages to the Nittany Valley's holy places.

Like a pilgrimage on Mount Nittany, the lower places in and around the valley can be visited, too. The locations for the legendary history and lore in this book can become genuinely legendary through an experience of your own. You can embark on an adventure to bring these legends to life.

These stories can be enjoyed alone, simply for the pleasure of the reading; for their intellectual curiosity. But a much more evocative and emotionally stimulating way to savor this legendary history is to actually go to the sites of the legends. Visiting each of the sites, as Chris Buchignani promises in his Introduction, will "take you on journeys into places where story and history, imagination and myth, as well as timeless feelings merge." In other words, the present, ever on the verge of becoming the future, will encounter the past—time will stop.

The Legends of the Nittany Valley can help you get there. On the following page is some information on each of the sites of the legends featured in this book. Visiting nittanyvalley.org will lead you to a detailed field guide for your adventures with precise locations, directions, and other information.

We, the living, are ever being called onto the field of action and away from comfortable passivity.

The Great Gitchie Manitou and Princess Nittany call out to you to visit their mountain. Pale Eyes is hoping, even if just for an afternoon, for a young man or woman to return her to her hollows. Wisamek's spirit awaits one more encounter with youth. And King Wi-Daagh, of course, will call out most fervently only once you depart the Nittany Valley, eagerly awaiting your return to a place you will always be able to call home.

I. Princess Nittany and Nittany Mountain

Areas: Mount Nittany, Gilliland Park, Laurel Gorge, Linden Hall, Stormstown, The Barrens

II. Accounts of Battles Affecting the Nittany Valley

Areas: McAlevys Fort in Hutingdon County, Tussey Mountain Ridge near Pine Grove Mills

III. The Legends of Penn's Cave

Area: Penn's Cave and Hotel in Centre Hall

IV. How the Indians Became Braves

Areas: Bald Eagle Mountain, Muncy in Lycoming County

V. The Passing Away of the Pennsylvania Indians

Areas: Pine Grove Mills, Centre Hall

VI. Why We Keep Returning to Happy Valley

A Portrait of
Henry Wharton Shoemaker

Dr. Simon J. Bronner

The following is adapted from Popularizing Pennsylvania: Henry
W. Shoemaker and the Progressive Uses of Folklore and History[1]
*by Dr. Simon J. Bronner. Dr. Bronner is Distinguished University
Professor of American Studies and Folklore at The Pennsylvania
State University, Harrisburg, and Director of the Doctoral Program
in American Studies.*

Imagine a life that includes safaris to Africa, climbs to the
world's highest peaks, time on the front lines of war, and audi-
ences with European royalty. Envision huge fortunes gained and

---

[1] Excerpted from: Bronner, Simon J., "Introduction" pages xiii-xxii and "A Rich
and Colorful Life" pages 1-2, in *Popularizing Pennsylvania: Henry W. Shoemaker and the Progressive Uses of Folklore and History*, 1996. Copyright © 1996 by
The Pennsylvania State University. Reprinted by permission of The Pennsylvania State University Press.

lost. Think about efforts going into bringing lions, wolves, elk, and other wild game into a private forest preserve stretching for 4,000 acres. From there you can help initiate and name a vast system of state forests, parks, camps, and trails. Amass barns full of museum-quality remnants of pioneer life—wagons, canoes, spinning wheels, guns, and much, much more. While you're at it, write more than 200 books and pamphlets, address thousands of groups, prepare a daily column, and manage four newspapers. Venture into the backwoods and collect ancient stories from the lips of old frontiersmen. From them create an elaborate mythology for a region that speaks for a nation and crusades for its redemption. Construct a social calendar that boasts visits from governors and senators and poor mountaineers with an old tale to tell. If you can imagine all that, you have an idea of the enormity of Henry Shoemaker's life.

Testimonies to Henry Wharton Shoemaker's contributions often refer to a "rich and colorful" past. "Col. Henry W. Shoemaker," one salute in the Harrisburg newspaper began, "has packed enough occupations and avocations into his life to provide sufficient material for a novel. As a banker, soldier, diplomat, publisher, historian and industrialist he may well be considered to have led a rich and colorful life." Sensitive about references to his wealth, he preferred to say he had a "long and prolific career" and often emphasized that his folklore-collecting from common people emerged from his early endeavors as his gritty "real life's work." At one point, he was described as "the greatest American reporter and the foremost living compiler of oral traditions in the United States." Beginning in business and diplomacy, he shifted to publishing and journalism while maintaining interests in local history, nature conservancy, and state politics. In his final position as State Folklorist, he combined previous work as archivist, journalist, government official, and, perhaps most significant, historian and conservationist.

If you've heard about the Pennsylvania mountains as a storied getaway, you can thank Henry Wharton Shoemaker. If you've ever enjoyed a state park or forest in Pennsylvania, give him some credit. If you've ever noticed a historical marker, you may be reading his words. Those Lions, Panthers, and Eagles you cheer on the field may have gained much of their association with Pennsylvania because of his efforts. The museum you visit, the memorial you honor, and the vista you admire may all have been touched by Henry Shoemaker's creative hand. That Pennsylvania legend you hear may just be the work of his imagination, and the curious place-name that grabs your attention could well have been his idea.

Few regions have had as energetic and influential a promoter as Henry Shoemaker. His campaign to popularize Pennsylvania and conserve its resources arose with a flurry during the Progressive Era, and he continued his unrelenting support through the New Deal and the post-World War II period. Proud of the "Progressive" label, and sounding some of its keywords of utility, efficiency, and public good, he made his mark within the Progressive movement by mobilizing private organizations and state programs for the "public use" of folklore, history, and nature to preserve America's cultural and natural heritage. The ways that this heritage became defined for ensuing generations, and the manner in which government became involved in the management of regional folklore, history, and environment, deserve attention in the ongoing discussion of American identity.

My exploration of Henry Shoemaker's life and career reveals how American and Pennsylvanian traditions were shaped and packaged to inspirit the land, provide a hedge against rapid industrialization, and instill civic values and regional pride. Drenched with religious symbolism, Shoemaker's campaign for conservation of folklore, history, and nature advanced America as a unified nation based on the principles of its founding in the wilderness. The cause encouraged patriotism, he claimed, and its literature underscored loyalty to the land by being imbued with a romantic regionalism that expressed the glory of the frontier and its common, hardy folk. The spiritual reverence Shoemaker and his supporters gave to the rustic past signaled a realization that the times had changed dramatically—and not all for the better—as a result of industrialization and immigration. Alarmed at the threat to the pristine land and the lore he adored, Shoemaker's answer was to promote Pennsylvania's image as the bucolic wonderland, to "see America first."

Beyond this intellectual concern, Henry Shoemaker's life story contains high drama worth recounting. He was born into one of America's wealthiest families in an exclusive area of New York City, and yet he came to champion the outdoor life of Pennsylvania's highlands. Mingling in the city's upper crust with Vanderbilts, Rockefellers, and Astors, he took to wandering off by himself on foot and horseback through treacherous backcountry trails, in addition to joining safaris in Africa and jaunts to Europe to meet royalty. He was already publishing his writings by the time he was eighteen, and began amassing collections of art and historical artifacts. He broke into Wall Street as one of its youngest brokers, and created a stir around town with his reported daredevil feats of mountain-climbing, ballooning, and airplaning. When he married, he enjoyed the most expensive wedding gift ever reported in America. A short time later, he suffered scandal in the front pages of the leading New York newspapers as his marriage disintegrated. Around the same time, he faced the tragic death of his younger brother and business partner. Henry Shoemaker served his country abroad as a diplomat and soldier, then returned to Pennsylvania to become a prominent newspaper publisher known for espousing Progressive Republican causes. He gained renown as an ardent conservationist and used his wealth to save forestland and threatened animals across the state of Pennsylvania. The romantic writer and the dedicated historian, he was also the urban sophisticate and backcountry roamer. He lost his family fortune and went to work for the state, again making his mark, becoming the nation's first State Folklorist. He died amid controversy over his use of folklore and history, but he left a lasting legacy of work for Pennsylvania's heartland.

It was my interest in the heartland's image and reality that led me to Henry Shoemaker's story. I consumed the popular image of Penn's Woods: farms, forests, and folk. I remember taking in those nationally broadcast Penn State games in "Nittany Valley," and I thrilled along with gazing millions when the blimp panned the gorgeous mountain vista. (And I wasn't alone in wondering, Exactly what is a Nittany lion?) Despite lingering industrial memories of coal mines and rust-belt mills, Central Pennsylvania—the "heart" and "highlands" of the state—carries the mystique of a place where hunters and fishermen enjoy nature's bounty. It is a storied place with countless small towns, ethnic varieties, and legends at every turn.

Think of the region's fame for hosting Amish, Mennonite, Jewish, French, Italian, Irish, and countless other ethnic-religious communities, and you see an epitome of tradition and tolerance. Standing squarely between distinct regions of New England and the South, Pennsylvania has a character—indeed, a mystique—all its own.

From one end of America to the other, even on foreign shores, people told me about Pennsylvania. Statements such as "The mountains are beautiful there," "That's where the Amish are," and "You have lots of folklore there" resounded in countless conversations. More than a state, the place appeared to be a cultural region unto itself. The longer I lived in Pennsylvania, the more I realized that this image, this mystique, is both fact and fiction. The state is not as unified, or as diverse, as the image suggests. The landscape is wilderness in spots, pastoral in others, scenic and stunning to be sure, but it is equally industrial and modern. In Lancaster County, the "garden spot" where so many tourists come attracted by Amish farmlands, commercial strips multiply, and in the mountains and the Black Forest region of Central Pennsylvania, the woods struggle to return to their pre-logging splendor. Many languages can be heard in the state, and residents are fiercely proud of their ethnic heritage, but in many communities tradition waits for revival as young people leaving for more prosperous pastures break the links of the generations.

As a resident of the state, as well as a cultural historian, I wanted to explain this romantic image. The narratives of rustic Pennsylvania abounded around me, and one especially seemed to capture the essence of this image. Tellers pointed to Mount Nittany, one of Pennsylvania's majestic picturesque peaks smack in the middle of the state, and began relating the saga of "the Indian Princess Nita-nee." She ran off for love with a French trapper, I was told, but her brothers caught up with the couple at the ledge over Penn's Cave and threw the Frenchman into the murky waters below. Since then, one could hear the sound of "Nita-nee" echoing through the area.

If I didn't perk up my ears for stories about "Nita-nee," I could read her story on postcards, advertisements, and promotions. Every summer it welcomes many thousands of visitors to Penn's Cave and is a favorite of generations of Penn State students studying in the shadow of Mount Nittany and walking by the famed Nittany Lion "shrine." And there were other similar stories, mystifying the mountains and streams of the mid-state. Often glorifying the original Indian inhabitants living in commune with nature, the romantic stories are complemented by countless Pennsylvania place names, such as Indian Grave Hill, Warrior Trail, and Picture Rocks. The stories might dwell on the ghosts of Indians past or recount incidents that bring pioneers in battle with nature, and adventurers in search of treasure, or tell of work-camp intrigue in the isolated mountains and forests. The imposing landscape of the mid-state lends an air of wonder and mystery that probably fostered tales of shifty ghosts and strange characters.

Romantic place-names, the "Nita-nee" story, and the romance of the Pennsylvania mountain lion were the work of Henry Shoemaker, who lived from 1880 to 1958. His own life was the stuff of legend as people talked about his immense wealth, his connections with royalty and power, his dramatic financial successes and failures, his daredevil cave explorations and mountain climbs, his brushes with death in the claws of wild animals, his eccentric hobbies, and above all, his consuming passion for conserving and promoting Pennsylvania's wildlife, mountains, and common folk. He was an intriguing character, who simultaneously gained renown and enjoyed obscurity.

Shoemaker led a "Progressive" campaign in the twentieth century to restore Penn's Woods and preserve the state as a cherished home to wildlife as well as folklife. Touting rugged frontier figures of Daniel Boone and Davy Crockett as the new American pantheon born of the wilderness, replacing the Old World classical heroes, Shoemaker and his Progressive cronies in the Boone & Crockett Club in New York City (led by Theodore Roosevelt and George Bird Grinnell) set out to explore and save the wilderness. By saving a source of American distinction and wonder, they believed, they could help recover a sense of American nationhood and spirituality at a time of rapid industrialization, immigration, and urbanization.

Shoemaker and his Progressive friends used their imaginations and their pens to promote a unified vision of America's genuine landscape and legend. It was a patriotic movement, Shoemaker often declared, to preserve the roots of America in the forested wilderness—and where better than in the only state with forests, or "sylvan," in its name? Not born in the state, he nonetheless trumpeted Pennsylvania as "God's Chosen wonderland," the "mystic region," a "wooded paradise," and a "glorious land of romance." His campaign is significant because while he was glorifying the abundance of the Pennsylvania wilderness his adopted state represented the heights of industrial transformation. After 1870, railroad, coal, oil, iron, steel, and lumber industries laid their claim to the state's land and people in dramatic fashion. As Pennsylvania's image went—rustic or industrial—so it seemed the nation's image would go.

At the forefront of conservation efforts during the Progressive Era, Shoemaker fell in with national leaders such as President Theodore Roosevelt, Governor Gifford Pinchot, Ernest Thompson Seton, Horace McFarland, Joseph Illick, and George Bird Grinnell, who encouraged American Victorians to commune with nature and appreciate its history and legend for future use. They believed that nature and related folk cultures held vitalizing, even spiritual, powers for a modern age. Roosevelt and Pinchot chimed the keyword "conservation" over the more passive "preservation," and Shoemaker energetically joined in, adding the spiritual resources of "history" and "folklore" to the list of endangered species meant for protection and use. In his newspaper editorials, in his books and many addresses, in his many organizations and state commissions, he lobbied for restoring the balance of nature, and the harmonious life and values it fostered. His special stand in this movement was somewhat ironic, for his wealth and power derived largely form the industrial boom of the late nineteenth century.

Henry Shoemaker took up the conservationist cause in Pennsylvania, where his family had derived a fortune from coal mining, banking, and railroading. His campaign was to convince Pennsylvanians to appreciate the beauty, heritage, and spirit of their natural surroundings, and consequently to prevent the kinds of development, industrial and materialistic, that threatened both the environment and the traditional social values associated with life in the wilderness. He spread this message in countless editorials, speeches, and writings carried all around the state, and in his official state duties on various commissions and boards. The publisher of newspapers in Reading, Altoona, Jersey Shore, and Bradford, he was also active in state and national politics, eventually becoming minister to Bulgaria. And as a prolific writer, he was the author of hundreds of pamphlets and books on nature, history, and folklore, and, counting his articles, columns, and addresses, his output probably ran into the thousands. He established and led numerous organizations designed to "sell Pennsylvania to Pennsylvanians," including the Pennsylvania Alpine Club, the Pennsylvania Folklore Society, the Pennsylvania Federation of Historical Societies and Museums, and the Pennsylvania Conservation Association.

An unabashed romantic and popularizer of legends and history, Shoemaker endured criticism and gained admiration for his version of Pennsylvania's heritage. He struggled to court scholarly bolstering for his endeavors, including support from Cornell's Harold Thompson, who dubbed him "Mr. Pennsylvania." His main allies, however, were fellow newspaper publishers who spread the mystique to their daily readers and to politicos who backed his efforts to involve state governments in the promotion of Pennsylvania as a special—indeed hallowed—place.

Residing only doors from the Governor's Mansion, Shoemaker, hobnobbed with politicians, bishops, and countless homespun "mountaineers." He represented the state as State Archivist, director of the State Museum, chairman of the State Historical Commission, and a member of the State Geographic Board and State Forest Commission. Politically, he received great notoriety from his appointment as minister to Bulgaria during the Hoover administration, but his crowning glory toward his goal of promoting Pennsylvania tradition was the distinction of being America's first official State Folklorist, a position that now exists in almost every state of the union. It was also the source of his greatest anguish as he battled for acceptance in his declining years. It is the development of cultural conservation and of the State Folklorist position that deserves special attention in any evaluation of the popularization of Pennsylvania, and I try to give it its due here.

For Henry Shoemaker, folklore represented the realm between history and fiction, nature and culture, and it got everyday people talking about themselves, their past, and their preindustrial surroundings. To him, folklore came from the spirited age of romance before "modern civilization" took over, and it reflected America's roots as the "glorious land of romance." With his booster spirit and popular goals, he found himself at odds with folklorists over what folklore was and how it should be presented. If he failed to woo scholars, he convinced his pals in government that promoting folklore perpetuated what Pennsylvania was all about—a modern-day Eldorado—and it became a centerpiece of a conservation and tourist program that jumped ahead of other industries of steel, coal, oil, and lumbering.

Eldorado. Legends of wealth in the wilderness. Henry Shoemaker claimed to have found the mythical kingdom sought after by sixteenth-century adventurers in the New World. His Eldorado lay in Central Pennsylvania between Philadelphia and Pittsburgh. Indeed, in Shoemaker's kingdom, urbanized and industrialized Philadelphia and Pittsburgh had little to do with Pennsylvania. The spiritual essence of Pennsylvania rested in the Pennsylvania highlands, and it had something of the Appalachian mystique for preserving its past and rusticity. But it had more cultures mixing in its midst, and it fed into, rather than borrowing from, southern Appalachian life. Pennsylvania was, Shoemaker wrote, "the final frontier of the modern complex civilization." Pennsylvania's Eldorado was a hunter's paradise filled with the charming powers of "natural wonders and historic spots," the spirits of ancient Indian wanderers, and the romance of legend filling every awe-inspiring mountain, stream, and forest.

The American "age of romance" that Shoemaker wanted to promote served to allay fears that America would be built over by a pernicious version of industrial capitalism. He worried that money and materialism were goals that overshadowed traditional values of civility and community. He saw the cities and their new residents that commanded the artificial light of industrialization as threats to America's unity and heritage. Like many other leaders who traced their roots to colonial immigration, Shoemaker was startled by the flood tide of immigrants from eastern and southern Europe sparked by turn-of-the-century industrialization. In the mythology of Shoemaker's wilderness, not only Pennsylvania, but also old Protestant America itself, was being promoted. Pennsylvania held the wilderness, the "frontier," that epitomized the original American consciousness of the invitation extended by the New World's fertile Eden. Shoemaker was hardly alone in believing that in such a place democratic principles and civil values thrived and that assimilation, or "Americanization," would be realized. In rhetoric that dripped old-time religion and evolutionary natural history, one could hear that from the mix of many pilgrim groups coming to the American Promised Land emerged a unique American type, a new Adam born of the Edenic wilderness. Shoemaker's distinction was his promoter's— some even said preacher's—zeal for spreading the good news in the marketing revolution brought by newspapers and periodicals around the turn of the century. Building a reverence for an imagined past that translated into Pennsylvania's special mystique,

Shoemaker used his newspapers as his pulpit and his stories as testament for a modern era.

Giving Pennsylvania this mystique was no mean feat. Henry Shoemaker began his campaign in the early twentieth century, when Americans felt more of a romantic inclination toward the frontier West or old New England. Pennsylvania was at that time America's industrial giant, and new factories, railroads, mines, and logging operations sprouted everywhere, so it seemed. Pennsylvania was America's future, it appeared, and new Roman Catholic, Eastern Orthodox, and Jewish immigrants from eastern and southern Europe flocked to its industries to supply an expanding America. Forests and mountains, and old traditions, were giving way before the allure of industrial profits. In this era of invention, Shoemaker and his cohorts fabricated a popular bucolic image to preserve the legendary spirit of Pennsylvania and to assimilate the state's new residents.

How successful, or desirable, was this campaign? That is a provocative question, and one that any account of Henry W. Shoemaker's life and work should address. Pennsylvania certainly draws people to visit its landscape and to consume its legends, but its image still lacks the regional recognition of the South and New England. Pennsylvania has had a mixed record of protecting its environment, and debates still rage about the privilege of industry and protecting folk cultures in the region. Signs of memorializing history and culture abound, and yet many residents question the effects of historical and cultural tourism. Shoemaker constantly advocated state management of history and culture much as government-administered parks or forests. He helped usher in the state's Historical Commission, and later the Pennsylvania Historical and Museum Commission—a groundbreaking agency in the nation's public history movement. Indeed, state government still takes great responsibility for protecting Pennsylvania's history and folklore, melded into "heritage," as natural resources. With the rise of multiculturalism as an educational concept, however, there is resistance to the promotion of an exceptional "state" heritage. One hears more today of a need for the state to return control of historical sites, and especially cultural property, to communities. At stake is the power to interpret, and control, a group's destiny as well as its past.

And what of Shoemaker's Progressive call for the public "management" of the wild? What of his belief that preserving the woods will foster a benevolent morality drawn from life in awe of nature? Pennsylvania usually leads the nation in number of hunting and fishing licenses issued, and it is among the nation's leaders in state park and forest acreage. Just as notable is that the state is the main arena for clashes between city and country values in little towns like Hegins, now known nationally for its annual pigeon shoot. (Shoemaker edited a book on the protection of pigeons), and between industry and the region in such places, and symbols, as Three Mile Island. Can it be said that the state's conflicts epitomize the nation's struggles?

Henry W. Shoemaker's vision for Pennsylvania has undergone much alteration. The major one was the addition—some even say the dominance—of the Amish and their farmlands in Lancaster County to the drawing spirit of Pennsylvania. Another Shoemaker, Alfred L., helped bring this legacy to public attention. At first Alfred was an ally, but he became Henry's bitter enemy, and that saga of their affection and disaffection is part of the drama surrounding the popularization of Pennsylvania. Moving beyond Henry Shoemaker's conser-vationist vision of Pennsylvania for Pennsylvanians, the "Dutch-land" brought non-Pennsylvanians to gaze on a variant of the Pennsylvania mystique. To Henry's chagrin in his last days, the "Dutchland" invited more development rather than less.

Another addition has been occurring as Pennsylvania's heavy industries became "history." The National Park Service, which first responded to Henry Shoemaker's conservationist campaign to protect the environment, now seeks to create what are called "Heritage Parks" revolving around industries in different regions of the state, such as oil, lumber, and coal. Designed for the purposes of economic development and supported by the state, the Heritage Parks program is intended to enhance "community, regional, and state-wide awareness and pride of Pennsylvania's historical and cultural legacy through the preservation, adaptive reuse, or restoration of historic sites and properties." The machine has entered Shoemaker's garden.

My accounting of Pennsylvania's popularization thus essentially involves the colorful life and pioneering work of Henry W. Shoemaker, the state's greatest promoter. I look at his ideas, sources, associates, and contributions. I especially cover his collection and fabrication of folklore because Shoemaker himself called it his "real life's work," and it provides a focus for analysis of the cultural conservationist cause that had national implications. Room still remains for analysis of Henry Shoemaker's contributions in the context of other intellectual concerns, but I believe that his use of folklore provides the most prominent point of departure for consideration of twentieth-century movements to define cultural tradition for a modern age. In the romantic promotion of folk tradition's connection to nature is found a new kind of spirituality that is still being explored, and exploited, today.

An Explanatory
by Henry W. Shoemaker

The following is excerpted from Henry W. Shoemaker's Explanatory Preface to Juniata Memories: Legends Collected in Central Pennsylvania, *published in Philadelphia in 1916. It is included as a means of insight on the mind and methodology of the author.*

In the summer of 1910, in the columns of the Newton Hamilton *Herald* these words were written by a correspondent: "There is one hope I have which I wish to give expression to. This beautiful Juniata Valley is rich in history and traditions. I should like to inspire some boy or girl to give this folklore to the world for the world's good. It will not be an easy task, but will require much digging and delving as it does to bring mineral wealth to the surface, and it will even more greatly enrich mankind."

At that time the correspondent had not heard of the compiler of the present volume, or the work he was trying to do. It was a year later that the writer of these pages began the task of collecting the legends and folklore of the Juniata Valley, and in the valleys tributary to it, such of it as survived into a materialistic age, or would be imparted by the holders of the secret treasure-chest.

It was not to be a final work, but merely to "blaze the trail" for others. Probably sixty legends were collected during the years 1911, 1912 and 1913. The first twenty-five or thirty came from the northerly limits of the region, in the Seven Mountains. The second half were unearthed in the Juniata Valley proper, or in the little valleys contiguous to it.

The first collection was compiled in book form, under the title of In the Seven Mountains, and secured a respectful hearing from the good people of the Juniata country from Altoona to Juniata Bridge. It was the first real encouragement that had come to the writer after ten years of effort to collect and publish the folklore of the Central Pennsylvania mountains. It was his sixth volume; he might have soon felt sensations of discouragement had it not been for the generosity of the dwellers by the "Blue Juniata."

The volume of legends pertaining to the southerly Juniata Valleys and the writer's eighth volume of Pennsylvania folklore is the one now being presented to the public—*Juniata Memories*. Most of the materials were gathered, as stated above, in 1911-1913, but several driving trips through the romantic territory, this "Eldorado Found," were taken in 1914 and 1915 to confirm certain details and local color.

The legends were secured from old people, hermits, farmers, lumbermen, teamsters, hostlers, hunters, trappers, old soldiers, and their ladies. They were freely given, many with the knowledge that some day they might find their way into print, some with no idea as to their future, told for the sheer joy of their relation. Many of them deal with persons of prominence in the political or social history of Central Pennsylvania, others with individuals of whom documentary history contains no trace—they of the "forgotten millions." They treat of Indian days principally, with a goodly sprinkling of the supernatural, of hunting, lumbering, and pioneering. Perhaps they are not representative legends of the Juniata Valley, better ones might have been found. The historian of the Juniata country, U.J. Jones, hinted of many such which the present writer could find no trace of. Those who knew them most probably died, failing to pass them on, long before the compiler of these chapters came on the scene.

But not finding any better legends, he has written out the twenty-six herein presented, which seemed to possess the most human interest, or as many as would fill a volume of this size. He has endeavored to reproduce them exactly as he heard them from the lips of the old people. They have not been enlarged on or changed, even when they ended abruptly or in mystery, but he fears that they have all lost much in passing through his hands.

There is an indefinable charm or thrill when hearing a tale of the long ago from an aged person, who knew the actors in it intimately, or whose family did, especially when it is recounted in an old farmhouse or mountain tavern on a blowy autumn night, before an open fire or even a glowing stove. As there is a place for all legends, there is also a time for hearing them.

The writer has visited practically every spot where the scenes in these legends are laid, he knows "the lay of the land." He could see the actors moving before him in his "mind's eye." As far as possible, he has tried to verify every date and incident, and to do so has absorbed a vast amount of Pennsylvania's history and literature. Some of the stories fit the page of history exactly, they must be absolutely true, others have no connection with anything recorded, they must represent the garbled memory of some one's animus or the mental vagaries of some tottering sage. Some of them would seem to clear up mooted points in history, others to further confuse it but all are a picture of a phase of life that is no more—the simple, imaginative, bold, free life of the frontier.

As stated previously, many of the characters are the ancestors of persons now prominent in the Juniata Valley or elsewhere. To avoid giving offense to these, as some of the ancient figures were most unjust to the redmen, and believed too much in ghosts, or that might was right, the compiler has reserved the privilege, as in his previous volumes, to occasionally change the names of persons, places and dates. But this has been done only when it seemed best, and always with deep regret. But if the legend occurred on the north side of a certain mountain, and not on the south slope, as stated in this book, it only matters a few miles, and what is that in the boundless space and endless time which make up this world? But it is a drawback to the exactitude of such a work.

There are countless legends still to be unearthed in Central Pennsylvania, especially in the valleys tributary to the Juniata. Some are mere fragments, just a word or two, others long enough to fill a volume, or be turned into historical novels. But all are worthy of being written down, saved from oblivion, before it is too late. Any one can find them, it requires no special gift, friendliness and simplicity, that is all.

They show the old pioneers in a favorable light for the most part, as possessing a decided *spiritual side* to their natures, far and above their abilities as mere hunters, trappers or wood-choppers. And in conclusion, first, and most of all, the old people are to be thanked for their kindness and patience in recounting the legends, their unvarying courtesy, that old-time charm that we must not let fade away. Then the press of the Juniata Valley, including the Newton Hamilton *Herald* prophet of this effort to collect these "memories," must be thanked, for they have been uniformly good to a writer in a new field. And the reading public are to be thanked, they have grasped at something they knew not what, and some of them found it to their liking. And lastly, but not least, to the great Pennsylvania Railroad, and its official photographer, Mr. W.H. Rau, of Philadelphia, who kindly granted the permission to reproduce the illustrations used in this book, go the author's sincere and lasting appreciation.

Henry W. Shoemaker
Member of American Folklore Society
April 29, 1916

Abridged Bibliography of
Henry W. Shoemaker

Immaterial Verses, 1898 (Verse)
Random Thoughts, 1899 (Verse)
Wild Life in Central Pennsylvania, 1903
Pennsylvania Mountain Stories, 1907
Pennsylvania Mountain Verses, 1907
Philosophy of Jake Haiden, 1911 (Editor)
More Pennsylvania Mountain Stories, 1912
Story of the Sulphur Spring, 1912
The Indian Steps, 1912
Tales of the Bald Eagle Mountains, 1912
Elizabethan Days, 1912 (Verse)
Susquehanna Legends, 1913
Stories of Pennsylvania Animals, 1913
Stories of Great Pennsylvania Hunters, 1913
In the Seven Mountains, 1914
The Pennsylvania Lion, 1914
Wolf Days in Pennsylvania, 1914
Black Forest Souvenirs, 1914
A Week in the Blue Mountains, 1914
Penn's Grandest Cavern, 1915
Pennsylvania Deer and Their Horns, 1915
A Pennsylvania Bison Hunt, 1915
Captain Logan, 1915
The Last of the War Governors, 1916
Juniata Memories, 1916
Pennsylvania Wildcats, 1916
Eldorado Found, 1916
Extinct Pennsylvania Animals Part I, 1916
Early Potters of Clinton County, 1916
North Mountain Mementos, 1920
Allegheny Episodes, 1922

Sources

Nit-A-Nee: A Tradition of a Juniata Maiden
Published: *Juniata Memories*, 1916
by Henry W. Shoemaker, As told by Jake Faddy

Nittany: The Legend of the Valley
Published: *LaVie* (Penn State University Yearbook), 1916

The Legend of Mount Nittany
Published: The Mount Nittany Conservancy
Authorship unknown, Date unknown

The Old Tree: The Tale of a Vanished Landmark
Published: *Juniata Memories*, 1916
by Henry W. Shoemaker, As told by Old Israel

The Indian Steps
Published: *The Indian Steps and Other Pennsylvania Mountain Stories*, 1912
by Henry W. Shoemaker

Love of the Planet Earth for the Planet Venus
Excerpted: *Allegheny Episodes*, 1922
by Henry W. Shoemaker

The Legend of Penn's Cave
Published: *Penn's Grandest Cavern*, 1915
by Henry W. Shoemaker, As told by Isaac Steele

Riding His Pony
Published: *Allegheny Episodes*, 1922
by Henry W. Shoemaker

The Birth of the Bald Eagles
Published: *Tales of the Bald Eagle Mountains*, 1912
by Henry W. Shoemaker

The Glory of Indian Summer
Published: *Tales of the Bald Eagle Mountains*, 1912
by Henry W. Shoemaker

The Indians' Twilight: The Story of Grandfather Pine
Published: *Allegheny Episodes*, 1922
by Henry W. Shoemaker, As told by Daniel Mark

King Widaagh's Spell
Published: *Tales of the Bald Eagle Mountains*, 1912
by Henry W. Shoemaker

Warrior's Mark: A Love Story
Published: *Juniata Memories*, 1916
by Henry W. Shoemaker, As told by Captain Logan

The Standing Stone: A Legend of the Ancient Oneidas
Published: *Juniata Memories*, 1916
by Henry W. Shoemaker

The Fountain of Youth
Published: *Penn's Grandest Cavern*, 1915
by Henry W. Shoemaker

Why the Seneca Would Not Eat Trout
Published: *Black Forest Souvenirs*, 1914
by Henry W. Shoemaker, As told by Billy Shongo and Jacob Fenstermaker

Poplar George
Published: *Allegheny Episodes*, 1922
by Henry W. Shoemaker, As told by a Grange Delegate

About Nittany Valley Press

Nittany Valley Press offers a special collection meant to foster a spirit of community across time for Penn Staters, Central Pennsylvanians, and friends. Nittany Valley Press encourages an appreciation for the history, customs, and spirit of Central Pennsylvania's Nittany Valley, the Pennsylvania State University, and nearby communities, offering select works that might serve to not only to welcome newcomers through an encounter with an historic spirit of place, but also as a means to conserve and perpetuate a lively, evergreen, and affectionate attitude toward Happy Valley as a place unlike any other. Discover other Nittany Valley Press books:

Conserving Mount Nittany by Tom Shakely

The Pennsylvania State College 1853-1932 by Erwin W. Runkle

Is Penn State a Real University? by Ben Novak

The Birth of the Craft Brew Revolution by Ben Novak

Reminiscences of Dr. F.J. Pond by Francis J. Pond